SRA

Open Court Reading

Book 2

Fossils

•

Courage

•

Our Country and Its People

SRA Open Court Reading

Book 2

Program Authors

Carl Bereiter
Marilyn Jager Adams
Marlene Scardamalia
Robbie Case
Anne McKeough
Michael Pressley
Marsha Roit
Jan Hirshberg
Ann Brown
Joe Campione
Iva Carruthers
Gerald H. Treadway, Jr.

SRA

A Division of The McGraw·Hill Companies

Columbus, Ohio

Acknowledgments

Grateful acknowledgment is given to the following publishers and copyright owners for permissions granted to reprint selections from their publications. All possible care has been taken to trace ownership and secure permission for each selection included.

Atheneum Books for Young Readers, Simon & Schuster Children's Publishing Division: A PLACE CALLED FREEDOM by Scott Russell Sanders, illustrations by Thomas B. Allen. *Text copyright © 1997, by Scott Russell Sanders. Illustrations copyright © 1997, by Thomas B. Allen.* Reprinted with permission of Atheneum Books for Young Readers, Simon & Schuster Children's Publishing Division. All rights reserved. JALAPENO BAGELS by Natasha Wing, illustrations by Robert Casilla. *Text copyright © 1996, by Natasha Wing. Illustrations copyright © 1996, by Robert Casilla.* Reprinted with permission of Atheneum Books for Young Readers, Simon & Schuster Children's Publishing Division. All rights reserved.

Barbara Bruno: "Monster Tracks" from Cricket the Magazine for Children, text and art copyright © 1991 by Barbara Bruno. Reprinted with permission of Barbara Bruno.

Children's Press, a division of Grolier Publishing Company, Inc.: IMMIGRANTS: COMING TO AMERICA by Gare Thompson. Copyright © 1997 by Children's Press. Reprinted by permission of Children's Press.

Clarion Books/Houghton Mifflin Co.: BRAVE AS A MOUNTAIN LION by Ann Herbert Scott. Text copyright © 1996 by Ann Herbert Scott. Illustrations copyright © 1996 by Glo Coalson. Reprinted by permission of Clarioin Books/Houghton Mifflin Co. All rights reserved.

Greenwillow Books, a division of William Morrow & Company, Inc.: "Iguanadon" from TYRANNOSAURUS WAS A BEAST by Jack Prelutsky. Copyright © 1988 by Jack Prelutsky. By permission of Greenwillow Books, a division of William Morrow & Company, Inc. "Seismosaurus" from TYRANNOSAURUS WAS A BEAST by Jack Prelutsky. Copyright © 1988 by Jack Prelutsky. By permission of Greenwillow Books, a division of William Morrow & Company, Inc.

Harcourt Brace & Company: Illustration from DINOSAURS by Lee Bennett Hopkins, which accompanies "Fossils" by Lilian Moore. Illustrations copyright © 1987 by Murray Tinkelman, reproduced by permission of Harcourt Brace & Company.

HarperCollins Publishers: "DRAGONS AND GIANTS" from FROG AND TOAD TOGETHER by ARNOLD LOBEL. COPYRIGHT © 1971, 1972 BY ARNOLD LOBEL. Used by permission of HarperCollins Publishers.

Holiday House: A PICTURE BOOK OF MARTIN LUTHER KING, JR. by David A. Adler, illustrated by Robert Casilla. Text copyright © 1989 by David A. Adler. Illustrations copyright © 1989 by Robert Casilla. All rights reserved. Reprinted by permission of Holiday House, Inc.

Henry Holt and Company, Inc.: *THE EMPTY POT,* WRITTEN AND ILLUSTRATED BY DEMI. Copyright © 1990 by DEMI.

Reprinted by permission of Henry Holt and Company, Inc.

ITP Nelson: "Courage" from HOCKEY CARDS AND HOPSCOTCH by Emily Hearn. Copyright © 1989 by Emily Hearn. Reprinted by permission of ITP Nelson.

Lothrop, Lee & Shepard Books, a division of William Morrow & Company, Inc.: NEW HOPE by Henri Sorensen. Copyright © 1995 by Henri Sorensen. By permission of Lothrop, Lee & Shepard Books, a division of William Morrow & Company, Inc. THE STORY OF THE STATUE OF LIBERTY by Betsy Maestro. Illustrated by Giulio Maestro. Text copyright © 1986 by Betsy C. Maestro. Illustrations copyright © 1986 by Giulio Maestro. By permission of Lothrop, Lee & Shepard Books, a division of William Morrow & Company, Inc.

Margaret K. McElderry Books, an imprint of Simon & Schuster Children's Publishing Division: "Statue of Liberty" by Myra Cohn Livingston. Reprinted with the permission of Margaret K. McElderry Books, an imprint of Simon & Schuster Children's Publishing Division from I NEVER TOLD AND OTHER POEMS by Myra Cohn Livingston. Copyright © 1992 Myra Cohn Livingston.

Morrow Junior Books, a division of William Morrow & Company, Inc.: A VERY IMPORTANT DAY by Maggie Rugg Herold. Illustrated by Catherine Stock. Text copyright © 1995 by Maggie Rugg Herold. Illustrations copyright © 1995 by Catherine Stock. By permission of Morrow Junior Books, a division of William Morrow & Company, Inc.

Orchard Books, New York: **From DREAMPLACE by George Ella Lyon, illustrated by Peter Catalonotto. Text copyright © 1993 by George Ella Lyon. Illustration copyright © 1993 by Peter Catalonotto. Reprinted by permission of Orchard Books, New York.**

Random House, Inc.: MOLLY THE BRAVE AND ME by Jane O'Connor, illustrations by Sheila Hamanaka. **Text Copyright © 1989 by Jane O'Connor. Illustrations copyright © 1990 by Sheila Hamanaka.** Reprinted by arrangement of Random House, Inc. "Life Doesn't Frighten Me" from AND STILL I RISE by Maya Angelou. Copyright © 1978 by Maya Angelou. Reprinted by permission of Random House, Inc.   T/A

Marian Reiner: "Fossils" from SOMETHING NEW BEGINS by Lilian Moore. Copyright © 1982 Lilian Moore. Used by permission of Marian Reiner for the author.

Scholastic Inc.: From THE HOLE IN THE DIKE by Norma Green, illustrated by Eric Carle. Text copyright © 1974 by Norma Green, illustrations copyright © 1974 by Eric Carle. Reprinted by permission of Scholastic Inc. From I SEE ANIMALS HIDING by Jim Arnosky. Copyright © 1995 by Jim Arnosky. Reprinted by permission of Scholastic Inc.   ALL

Steck Vaughn Company: DINOSAUR FOSSILS by Dr. Alvin Granowsky. Copyright © 1992 by Steck Vaughn Company. Used by permission.

Tambourine Books, a division of William Morrow & Company Inc.: THE BUTTERFLY SEEDS by Mary Watson. Copyright 1995 by Mary Watson. By permission of Tambourine Books, a division of William Morrow & Company Inc.

Viking Penguin, a division of Penguin Putnam Inc.: From THE DINOSAUR WHO LIVED IN MY BACKYARD by B.G. Hennessy, pictures by Susan Davis. Copyright © 1988 by Susan Davis, illustrations. Used by permission of Viking Penguin, a division of Penguin Putnam Inc.

SRA/McGraw-Hill

A Division of The McGraw·Hill Companies

Send all inquiries to:
SRA/McGraw-Hill
250 Old Wilson Bridge Road
Suite 310
Worthington, Ohio 43085

Printed in the United States of America.

ISBN 0-02-830953-7

1 2 3 4 5 6 7 8 9 VHP 04 03 02 01 00 99

Program Authors

Carl Bereiter, Ph.D.
University of Toronto

Marilyn Jager Adams, Ph.D.
BBN Technologies

Michael Pressley, Ph.D.
University of Notre Dame

Marsha Roit, Ph.D.
National Reading Consultant

Robbie Case, Ph.D.
University of Toronto

Anne McKeough, Ph.D.
University of Toronto

Jan Hirshberg, Ed.D.

Marlene Scardamalia, Ph.D.
University of Toronto

Ann Brown, Ph.D.
University of California at Berkeley

Joe Campione, Ph.D.
University of California at Berkeley

Iva Carruthers, Ph.D.
Northeastern Illinois University

Gerald H. Treadway, Jr., Ed.D.
San Diego State University

Table *of* Contents

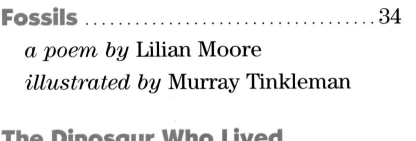

Table *of* Contents

Table *of* Contents

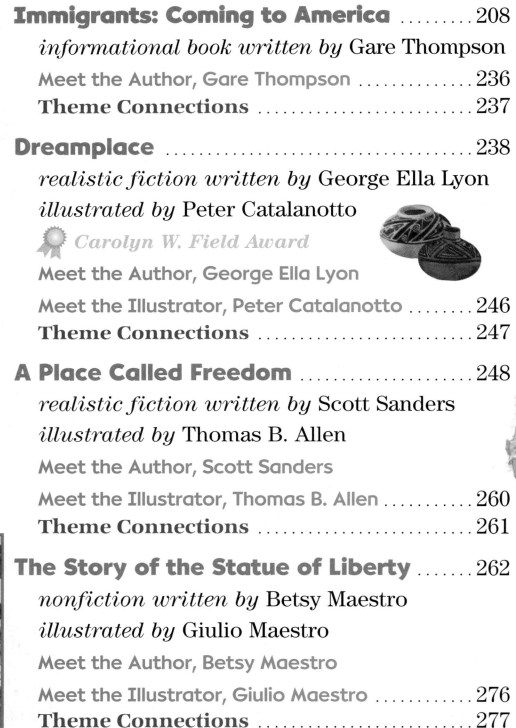

10

Fossils

How do you know things like dinosaurs lived many, many years ago? How can we tell how big they were or what they looked like? Fossils can be the keys to the past. Find out what scientists see in fossils of long ago.

Dinosaur Fossils

by Dr. Alvin Granowsky

We have learned all that we know about dinosaurs from their fossils. A fossil is what is left of a plant or an animal that lived long ago.

Fossils can be leaves, shells, eggs, or skeletons. Some fossils are hardened tracks or footprints left by a moving animal.

When a plant or animal dies, it can become covered with mud or sand. As time goes by, the plant or animal becomes covered by many layers of mud and sand. After thousands of years, the bottom layers harden into rock. The dead plant or animal also hardens into rock. This is how fossils are formed.

Any plant or animal can become a fossil. Animal fossils are usually hard parts of the body such as teeth, bones, or shells.

Sometimes an animal's whole body is frozen in ice or covered very quickly with river mud. Then scientists can study the skin and other soft parts of an animal's body.

Sometimes fossils are found by chance. Fossils may be uncovered by workers digging a well or roadway.

Most often, scientists who study fossils have to spend a long time looking for them. These scientists are called paleontologists.

Fossils found in soft ground are the easiest ones to collect. Paleontologists can dig them out with a shovel or by hand.

Fossils have to be loosened slowly from rocks. Scientists use chisels, hammers, or picks to remove the fossils. They work carefully to protect the fossils.

Then the hardest work begins. Most fossils are found in pieces. The bones are like the pieces of a puzzle. Putting the bones together is difficult when some of the pieces are missing.

What if some of the fossil pieces don't belong? That often happens when the fossils of many animals are found in the same place.

Sometimes scientists make mistakes when they work with fossils. At one time, they thought the thumb-claw of an Iguanodon was a horn on its nose.

But scientists learn from their mistakes. They work until they find the right way to put the bones together. The skeletons are placed in museums so that everyone can learn about dinosaurs.

Scientists must learn about dinosaurs from fossils because dinosaurs are extinct. When scientists say that dinosaurs are extinct they mean that dinosaurs are not alive today.

For a long time, we didn't know that dinosaurs had ever lived. Then dinosaur fossils were found. Scientists learned that dinosaurs had once lived all over Earth.

When the first dinosaur fossils were found, people wondered, "What kind of bone is this?"

People saw how big the bones were. They asked, "Could these be the bones of an elephant?"

Putting together dinosaur bones was slow work. Scientists tried putting the bones together in different ways.

If some of a dinosaur's bones were missing, the job was even slower. Sometimes scientists had to guess what the missing parts looked like.

At one time, scientists thought they
had discovered a new dinosaur called a
Polacanthus. Scientists had only part of the
skeleton, but they tried to imagine what a
Polacanthus looked like. They thought that
the Polacanthus had a small head and spikes
along its back.

But later, scientists found other bones that
belonged to the same skeleton. With the new
bones, scientists could see that the skeleton
was from a Hylaeosaurus.

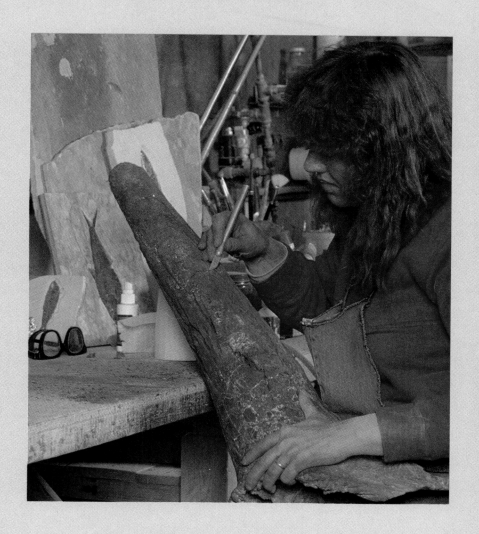

Sometimes scientists find many dinosaur bones in one place. In Wyoming, scientists discovered several complete skeletons of Camptosaurus dinosaurs. That made it easier to describe a Camptosaurus. After studying the skeletons, scientists decided that the Camptosaurus grew as long as 23 feet.

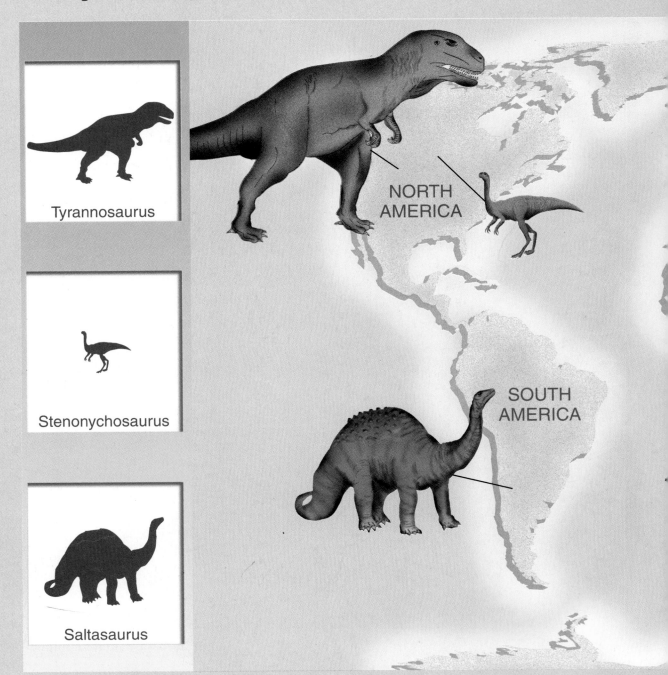

Tyrannosaurus

Stenonychosaurus

Saltasaurus

NORTH AMERICA

SOUTH AMERICA

Dinosaur fossils have been found in many places around the world. That is how we know that dinosaurs once lived all over Earth. This map shows where the fossils of some kinds of dinosaurs were found.

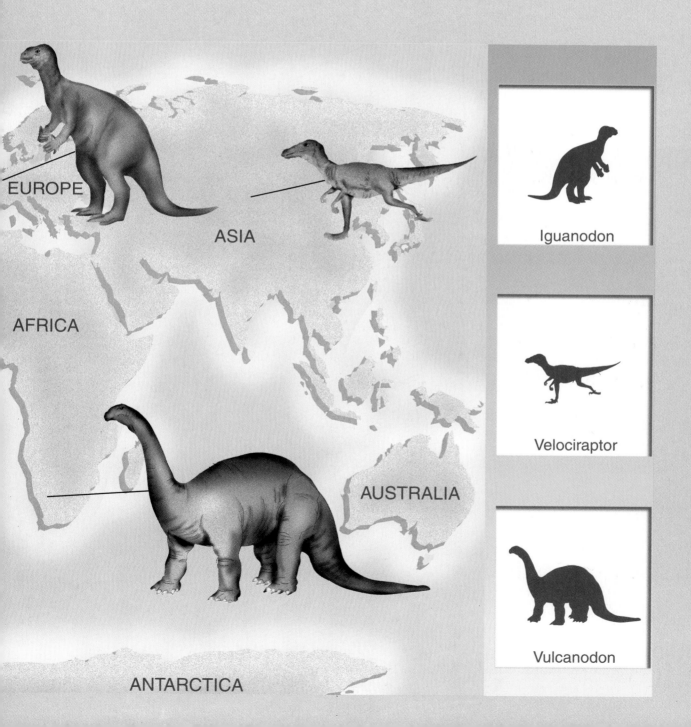

EUROPE

ASIA

AFRICA

AUSTRALIA

ANTARCTICA

Iguanodon

Velociraptor

Vulcanodon

29

Dinosaur bones show us that there were dinosaurs of all shapes and sizes. The skeletons scientists put together help us see how different each kind of dinosaur was.

The skeleton of a Tyrannosaurus Rex stands on two legs and has big, sharp teeth. The skeleton of an Apatosaurus shows its long, thin neck and tail.

New fossils are still being found today. Someday you could be a scientist and put together a dinosaur skeleton.

Dinosaur Fossils

Meet the Author

Dr. Alvin Granowsky tested his story ideas for "Dinosaur Fossils" on his young grandson, who really liked dinosaurs and fossils. Dr. Granowsky finds the subject of dinosaurs very exciting. Dinosaurs have been around for a very long time, but new things are still being learned about them.

Dr. Granowsky also likes to tell stories from another point of view. For example, in the story of Cinderella he likes to tell the story from the stepsisters' point of view. He said, *"When I am writing . . . I like to sneak in something that would make someone smile or think."*

Theme Connections

Think About It

"Dinosaur Fossils" tells us about fossils and the scientists who study them. Here are questions to discuss:

- What are fossils?
- What does the story teach us about how fossils are formed?
- Why are fossils important discoveries?

Post any questions you have about fossils on the Concept/Question Board.

Record Ideas

Record in your Writing Journal some thoughts you have about fossils.

Make a Chart

Create a chart for recording information from "Dinosaur Fossils."

- At the top of the first column, write "General Idea." Then, in that column, write a few sentences telling the general idea of the story.
- In the next three columns, give some examples.
- Your chart might look like this:

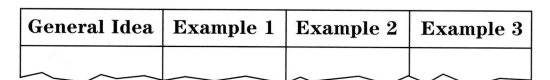

General Idea	Example 1	Example 2	Example 3

Fossils

Lilian Moore
illustrated by Murray Tinkelman

Older than
books,
than scrolls,

older
than the first
tales told

or the
first words
spoken

are the stories

in forests that
turned to
stone

in ice walls
that trapped the
mammoth

in the long
bones of
dinosaurs—

the fossil
stories that begin
Once upon a time

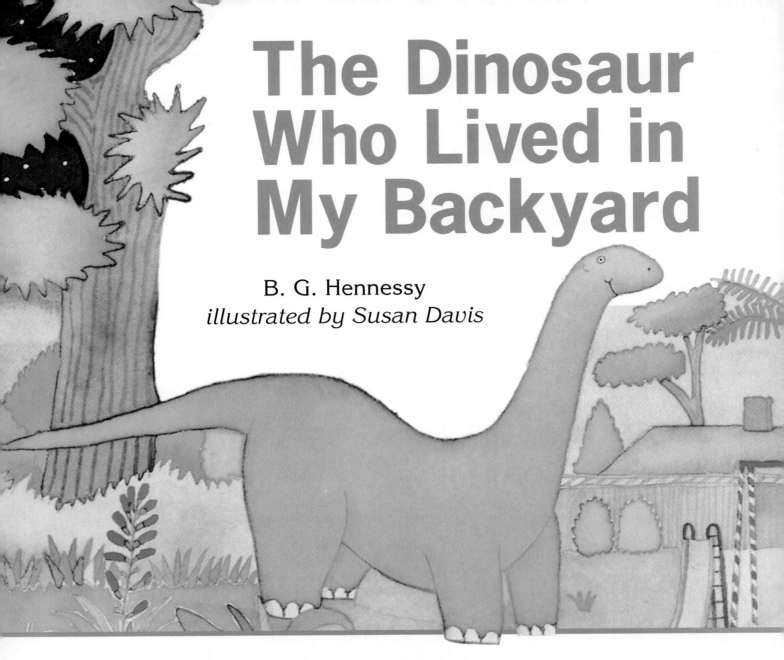

The Dinosaur Who Lived in My Backyard

B. G. Hennessy

illustrated by Susan Davis

There used to be a dinosaur who lived in my backyard. Sometimes I wish he still lived here. The dinosaur who lived here hatched from an egg that was as big as a basketball.

By the time he was five, he was as big
as our car.

Just one of his dinosaur feet was so big
it wouldn't even have fit in my sandbox.

My mother says that if you eat all your vegetables you'll grow very strong. That must be true, because that's all this dinosaur ate. I bet he ate a hundred pounds of vegetables every day. That's a whole lot of lima beans.

This dinosaur was so heavy that he would have made my whole neighborhood shake like pudding if he jumped. He weighed as much as twenty pick-up trucks.

The dinosaur who lived in my backyard
was bigger than my schoolbus. Even
bigger than my house.

He had many other dinosaur friends.
Sometimes they played hide-and-seek.
Sometimes they had terrible fights.

The dinosaur who used to live here was allowed to sleep outside every night. It's a good thing he didn't need a tent. He was so big he would have needed a circus tent to keep him covered.

Back when my dinosaur lived here,
my town was a big swamp. This dinosaur
needed a lot of water. If he still lived
here we'd have to keep the sprinkler on
all the time.

My dinosaur had a very long neck so he could eat the leaves at the top of trees. If he still lived here, I bet he could rescue my kite.

That's all I know about the dinosaur who used to live in my backyard.

He hasn't been around for a very long
time. Sometimes I wish he still lived here.
    It would be pretty hard to keep a
dinosaur happy.
    But my sister and I are saving all our
lima beans—just in case.

The Dinosaur Who Lived in My Backyard

Meet the Author

B. G. Hennessy worked as a book designer and an art director for children's books. She began writing books when her first child was learning to talk. As she writes, she thinks about how the picture would look. She tries to give the illustrator something to work with. She wrote her first book when she was five years old. She still has this book and often reads it to children in schools.

Meet the Illustrator

Susan Davis always wanted to do children's books. Unlike many other artists who studied art in school, she studied art on her own. She said, *"The important thing in illustrating a book is to be patient."* "The Dinosaur Who Lived in My Backyard" took two years to illustrate. She wanted to show the dinosaur doing all sorts of things. She has also illustrated other children's books.

Theme Connections

Think About It

This story combined fantasy and facts. Here are some questions to discuss:

- Is it possible that a dinosaur really lived in the boy's backyard? Why or why not?
- What does the story teach us about how and where dinosaurs lived?
- How did this story help you connect dinosaurs to the world today?

Check the Concept/Question Board and answer any questions you can. Post any new questions you have.

Record Ideas

Record in your Writing Journal some ideas about the story you talked about with others. You may list your ideas as notes or in a chart.

Make a Chart

- Make a chart comparing a dinosaur's life and your life.
- You may include information about foods eaten, places to sleep, or size.
- Your chart might look like this:

Dinosaurs	Me
Slept outside	Slept inside

Iguanodon

Jack Prelutsky
illustrated by Daniel Moreton

Iguanodon, Iguanodon,
whatever made you fade,
you've traveled on, Iguanodon,
we wish you could have stayed.

Iguanodon, Iguanodon,
we've sought you everywhere,
both here and yon, Iguanodon,
but failed to find you there.

Iguanodon, Iguanodon,
you were a gentle kind,
but now you're gone, Iguanodon,
and left your bones behind.

Seismosaurus

Jack Prelutsky
illustrated by Daniel Moreton

Seismosaurus was enormous,
Seismosaurus was teremendous,
Seismosaurus was prodigious,
Seismosaurus was stupendous.

Seismosaurus was titanic,
Seismosaurus was colossal,
Seismosaurus now is nothing
but a monumental fossil.

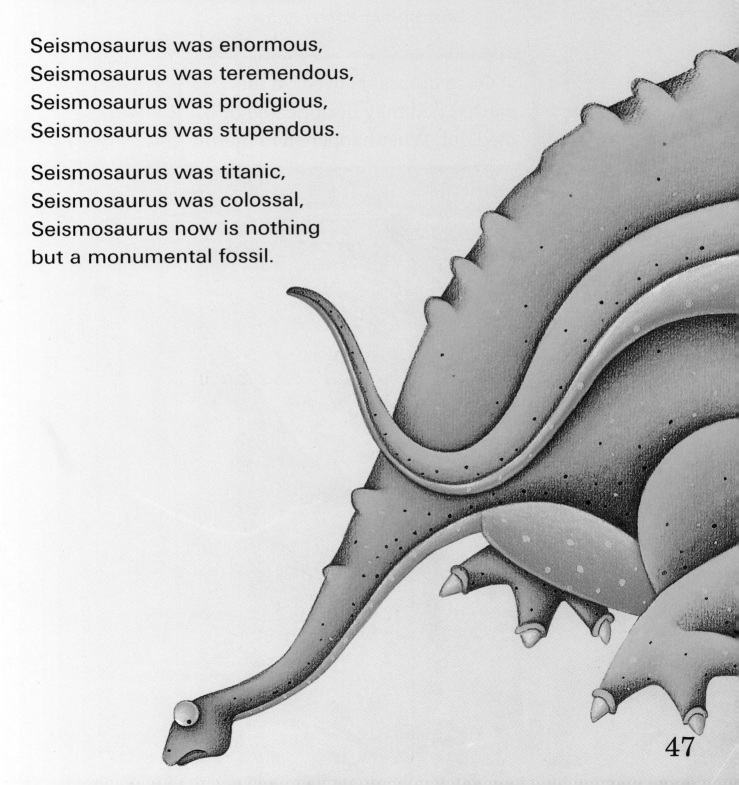

Why Did the Dinosaurs Disappear?

Karen Sapp

illustrated by Robert Frank

Once dinosaurs lived on the earth. Then they disappeared or died out. What happened to them?

Many other animals, including animals that lived in the sea and animals that flew through the air also died out. Many plants died too.

No one knows for sure what happened, but scientists have some ideas.

Some scientists think that new kinds of plants started growing because of changes in the climate. Their idea is that these plants poisoned dinosaurs that ate them. Then meat-eating dinosaurs starved to death when they could not find plant-eating dinosaurs to eat. There is a problem with this idea. Only land animals would have eaten the poisonous plants, but sea animals died, too. Besides, this idea does not explain why some kinds of plants also died out.

Did other animals cause the death of the dinosaurs? Maybe small animals stole and ate dinosaur eggs before they could hatch. This would explain what happened to dinosaurs that laid eggs. But what about dinosaurs that were born live? What about the sea animals and plants that died, too?

Many scientists think that the dinosaurs died out because the earth became very cold. Most dinosaurs could not live in very cold weather. They did not have fur or feathers to keep them warm. Dinosaurs were so huge they could not burrow into the ground for warmth and protection. But what could make the weather become so cold?

The earth long ago was not at all like it is today. Huge earthquakes made the water in the oceans rise and fall many times. When the water level fell, there was more moisture in the air. This caused more rain and colder weather. The earthquakes also made volcanoes erupt all over the world. Some scientists think that a giant volcano in the part of the world we now call India erupted for many, many years!

All this time, it blew so much ash and dust into the air that the sun's rays could not reach the earth. Imagine what it would be like never to see the sun! The earth grew very cold. Plants died without the sunlight. Without plants to eat, the plant-eating dinosaurs died. Then the meat-eaters died.

In 1978, a new discovery gave some scientists another idea about why the earth became so cold.

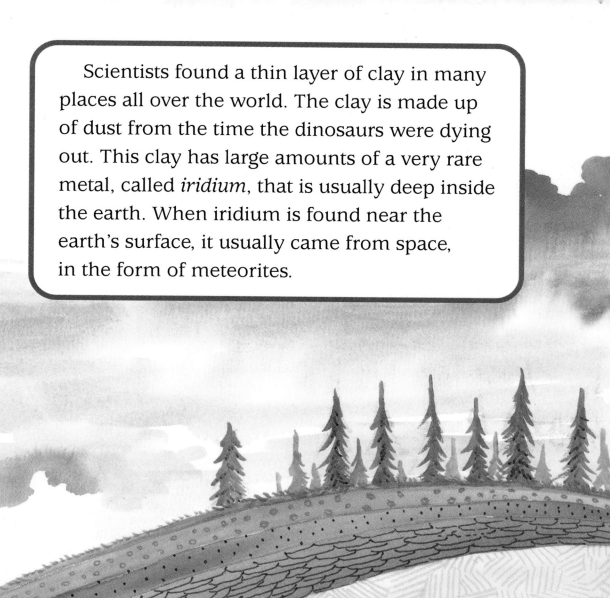

Scientists found a thin layer of clay in many places all over the world. The clay is made up of dust from the time the dinosaurs were dying out. This clay has large amounts of a very rare metal, called *iridium*, that is usually deep inside the earth. When iridium is found near the earth's surface, it usually came from space, in the form of meteorites.

Meteorites are chunks of stone or metal that have crashed to the earth. Most of the time, meteorites do not hit the earth hard enough to do much damage. Sometimes, though, a very large meteorite crashes. When this happens, it makes a huge hole, or *crater*, in the ground.

In 1980, a crater was found in Mexico. Scientists think the crater was made about the time the dinosaurs disappeared. They think the meteorite that caused this crater was 6 miles long.

North America

Mexico

Gulf of Mexico

Mexico City

Mérida

Campeche

Pacific Ocean

South America

Imagine something that big hitting the earth! It would blast millions of tons of dust and rock into the sky. Heat caused by the crash would start many fires. The smoke from those fires would add soot to the air. (Scientists found large amounts of soot mixed in with the iridium.)

The thick cloud of dust, rock, and smoke would swirl around the world, blocking the sunlight for months or even years. Without sunlight, the earth would grow very cold. When the dust finally settled, it would form a layer of clay, and in the clay there would be large amounts of iridium. This is exactly what some scientists think happened. Again, their idea is that the lack of sunshine caused dinosaurs and other life forms to die.

Some scientists think that both the volcano idea and the meteorite idea could be correct. There are two ways this might work. One is that a meteorite might have hit the earth hard enough to make the volcanoes erupt. Another way is that the volcanoes could have been erupting for many years, slowly killing plants and animals. Then, when a meteorite hit, it quickly finished the job.

No one really knows for sure why the dinosaurs disappeared, but many scientists are still trying to find out.

Why Did the Dinosaurs Disappear?

Meet the Illustrator

Robert Frank was born in Argentina and moved to the United States during World War II. He grew up in New York City and pursued his interests in art throughout his youth. Attending the High School of Industrial Arts, he went on to study illustration and advertising.

Robert now teaches art at the same school he attended, while he continues to work on freelance illustration projects. He lives in New Jersey with his wife and young daughter and collects antiques as a hobby.

Theme Connections

Think About It

Scientists have many different theories about why the dinosaurs disappeared. Here are some questions to think about and discuss:

- What new information did you learn about why the dinosaurs disappeared?
- How do fossils help scientists form theories about the disappearance of the dinosaurs?
- Why is the disappearance of the dinosaurs so interesting to scientists and others?

Check the Concept/Question Board and answer any questions you can. Post any new questions you have about the theme Fossils.

Record Ideas

 Record any new ideas about fossils or how dinosaurs disappeared in your Writing Journal.

Make a List

- Write a theory for the answer to a question that you have about fossils.
- Discuss with a classmate or with someone at home why your theory is a good one, as well as any problems you find with it.
- Make a list of all the reasons it is a good theory
- Then, make a list of any problems you discover.

FINE Art

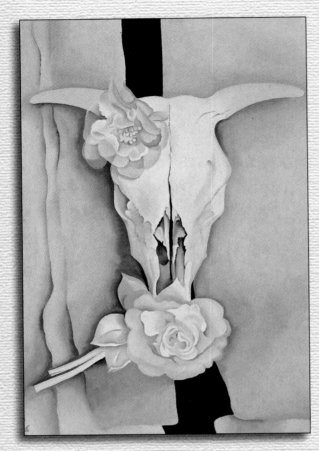

Cow's Skull with Calico Roses. 1932.
Georgia O'Keeffe. Oil on canvas. 91.2 × 61 cm.
The Art Institute of Chicago, Gift of Georgia
O'Keeffe. © 1999 The Georgia O'Keeffe
Foundation/Artist's Right Society (ARS),
New York. Photograph © 1998, The Art Institute
of Chicago, All Rights Reserved.

Desert Still Life. 1951.
Thomas Hart Benton.
Tempera with oil on linen
mounted on panel. Bequest of
the artist, The Nelson–Atkins
Museum of Art, Kansas City,
Missouri. F75–21/45. ©1999
Thomas Hart Benton and Rita
P. Benton Testamentary
Trust/Licensed by VAGA,
New York, NY.

Fossil of an extinct ancestor of the crayfish, found in the Hummelberg Quarry, Solnhofen, Germany.
Photo: © Jonathan Blair/Corbis.

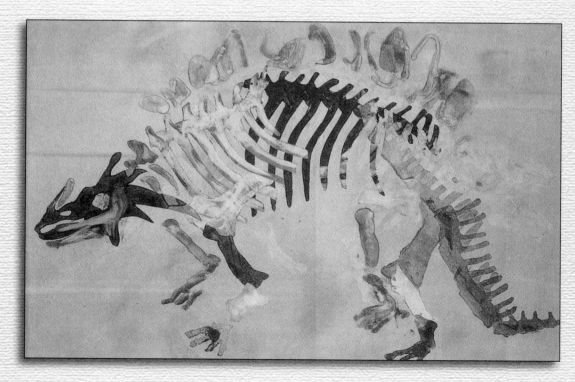

Dinosaur. 1980. **Mary Frank.** Color monotype. 24.75 × 35.5 in. Collection of The Whitney Museum of American Art. Purchase, with funds from the Print Committee. 83.13.

Monster Tracks

by Barbara Bruno

Snarl. Splash. Plop. Eek! Crunch. Just how did those bones and footprints come to be in these fossil rocks—rocks that tell a wordless story lost in time?

Sand-cast your own fossil clues from a past when monsters roamed and left odd tracks and dinner crumbs in the prehistoric ooze. First gather some feathers, twigs, bones (fish bones are fun), seashells, stones, or small sharp rocks to imprint or embed in sand.

Along with this interesting assortment of objects, you'll also need enough plaster of Paris to fill a mold, sand for shaping the mold, and a container. A plastic-lined, shallow cardboard box works well.

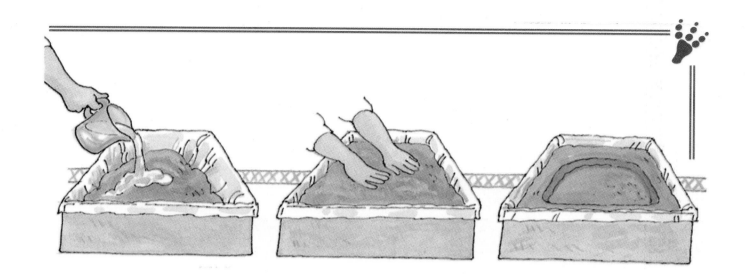

Wet the sand enough so that it keeps its shape when squeezed into a ball, then pack it into the box. Scoop out a flat area about an inch deep and as large as you want your fossil rock to be. Smooth the surface. You're ready to begin sand-casting.

To form the mold you must think in reverse. Holes poked in the sand will stick out. Sunken areas, like footprints, must be built up in the sand. Textures and other features can be made by pressing different objects into the sand. Seashells, bones, and other objects to be left in the sand casting must be pressed facedown into the sand. That way they'll rise above the finished casting's surface. (Half-buried things are interesting, too.)

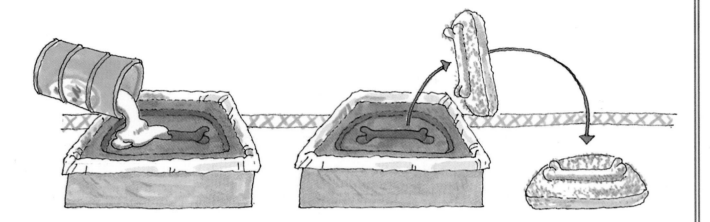

When you have finished
making the mold, mix the plaster
according to the instructions on
the box. Mix only the amount
you'll need to fill the mold. Slowly
pour the plaster into the deepest
parts of the mold first so that
trapped air won't spoil the sand
casting. Then
carefully fill
the rest of
the mold.

When the sand casting has hardened completely (about fifteen minutes, depending on its size and thickness), carefully dig it up. Gently brush away as much of the sand as you can. Some sand will remain embedded in the plaster.

Your sand casting most likely won't look exactly as you expected, but the results are always fun to see. You can "age" your fossil rock by painting it with watercolors or rubbing mud into the deepest imprints.

Monster Tracks

Meet the Author and Illustrator

Barbara Bruno is a writer, author, and photographer. She studied art at the Philadelphia College of Art. She has illustrated over fifty craft articles for a magazine for children called *Cricket*. She lives in New Jersey.

Theme Connections

Think About It

"Monster Tracks" tells how to make your own fossil. Here are some questions to think about and discuss:

- What does the selection teach us about how fossils are created?
- Do you think fossils are being made today? Why or why not?
- Why are fossils important discoveries?

Check the Concept/Question Board and answer any questions you can.

Record Ideas

Record in your Writing Journal any new ideas you have about fossils after talking with others. You may list your ideas as notes or in a chart.

Make a Story

Make up a story to go with the fossil you made after reading "Monster Tracks."

- Pretend that the fossil you made is real.
- Describe the living thing that created the imprint.
- Tell where it lived and what it needed to survive.
- Explain how and where you found the fossil.

Bibliography

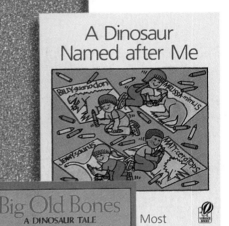

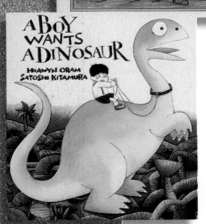

A Dinosaur Named After Me

by Bernard Most. Are you named after a dinosaur? Ryan, Amy, Eric, and Katy are! Who else?

Big Old Bones

by Carol Carrick. Professor Potts is having trouble putting together some old bones he found out West. Can you help him out?

Digging Up Dinosaurs

by Aliki. How do those dinosaur bones get into the museum anyway? If you've ever asked that question, this book has the answers.

A Boy Wants a Dinosaur

by Hiawyn Oram. Alex thinks he would like a dinosaur for a pet, but he realizes that it might just be too much trouble.

Dinosaur Hunters

by Kate McMullan. How do scientists find out what prehistoric animals were like? Read this book to find out.

Dinosaur for a Day

by Jim Murphy. Imagine you are a dinosaur mother with eight hungry children to feed. What would you do?

Saturday Night at the Dinosaur Stomp

by Carol Shields. Have you ever wondered what caused the first earthquake? Read about this dinosaur dance that really sets off some fireworks!

Time Train

by Paul Fleischman. Miss Pym and seven students are headed to Utah for spring break but it looks like they might have taken a wrong turn. Where are they?

Do you have to be a hero to have courage? Or can courage mean giving an answer in class when you are not sure you are right? Maybe courage can be both of these things. What do you think?

Molly the Brave and Me

Jane O'Connor
illustrated by Sheila Hamanaka

Molly has guts. She has more guts than anybody in the second grade. She can stand at the top of the monkey bars on one foot.

She doesn't mind it when Nicky hides dead water bugs in her desk.

And if big kids pick on her, Molly tells them to get lost.

Molly is so brave. I wish I was like her.

Today on the lunch line Molly said to me, "Beth, can you come to our house in the country this weekend? It is lots of fun there."

Wow! I guess Molly really likes me. That made me feel good.

But I have never been away from home. What if I get homesick? What if they eat stuff I don't like?

What if there are lots of wild animals? I was not sure I wanted to go.

I sat at a table with Molly. I said, "Gee, Molly. It sounds neat. Only I don't know if my parents will say yes."

That night Molly's mom called my mom. My mom said yes. So how could I say no? It was all set. Molly's parents were going to pick me up on Saturday morning.

Friday night I packed my stuff. Later my mom tucked me in bed. "I'm scared I'll miss you," I said. "I bet I'll cry all the time. Then Molly will think I'm a big baby. And she won't like me anymore."

My mom hugged me. "You will have fun. And Molly will understand if you are a little homesick." Then my mom kissed me two times. "One kiss is for tonight. The other is for tomorrow night when you will be at Molly's house."

Molly's parents came early the next
morning. I was scared, but I was excited,
too. Most of all I did not want to look like a
wimp around Molly. So I waved good-bye to
my parents and hopped in the back seat.

Molly's dog sat between us. "This is Butch," said Molly. Right away Butch started licking me. I'm kind of scared of big dogs. But did I show it? No way! I acted like I loved getting dog spit all over my face!

By noon we got to Molly's house. It sat all alone at the top of a hill. "This was once a farm," Molly's mom told me. "It's 150 years old."

I like new houses. They haven't had time to get any ghosts. But I didn't say that to Molly's mom.

Right after lunch we went berry picking. That sounded like fun. Then I saw all the beetles on the bushes.

I did not want to touch them. But Molly just swatted them away. So I gave it a try too. "Hey! this is fun," I said. "I have never picked food before."

We ate lots and lots of berries. Red juice got all over my face and hands. I pretended it was blood and I was a vampire.

I chased Molly all around. "You know what?" I told her. "I am really glad that I came to your house."

Later we went looking for wild flowers. That sounded nice and safe to me. We walked all the way down to a stream. A big log lay across the stream.

Molly ran right across it. Boy, what guts! Butch ran across too. I stared at the log. "Aren't there any wild flowers on this side?" I asked.

Molly shook her head. "The best ones are over here. Come on, Beth. Don't be scared. Just walk across—it's easy."

"Okay," I told myself. "Quit acting like a wimp." I started taking tiny steps across the log. Near the end I slipped.

Oof! Down I went. "Are you all right?" Molly asked.

I nodded, but my backside really hurt.

We picked flowers for a while. And when we left, I crawled across the log. Molly didn't tease me. Still I knew I looked like a jerk.

On the way back to the house Butch saw a rabbit and chased it into a field of corn. "Dumb dog!" said Molly. "He will never catch that rabbit. We'd better go and find him."

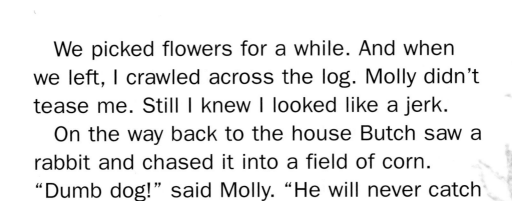

"Oh, rats!" I thought, but I went in after Molly. We followed the sound of Butch's barks. Boy, was that field big! The corn was way over our heads and it seemed to go on for miles.

At last we spotted Butch. Molly ran and hugged him. Then she pulled me by the arm. "This place is creepy," Molly said. "Let's get out of here."

That was fine with me! But it was not so easy getting out. All the corn looked the same. It was hot and hard to see. Bugs kept flying in our faces. It felt like we were walking around and around in circles.

"Can't Butch help us find the way?" I asked.

Molly shook her head. "Butch can't find his own doghouse."

Then Molly started blinking hard. And her nose got all runny. "Beth," she said. "We're really stuck in here. I'm scared."

Molly scared? I could not believe it! I held her hand. "Don't be scared," I told her, even though I was scared too. "We'll get out of here."

Then I got an idea. "Come on," I told Molly. I started to walk down the space between two rows of corn. I did not make any turns. I stayed in a straight line.

"Pretend this is a long street," I said. "Sooner or later we have to come to the end of it."

And at last we did! Molly and I hugged each other and jumped up and down. Woof! Woof! went Butch. "Hot stuff!" said Molly. "You got us out."

When we got back to Molly's house, her mother said, "Where have you girls been? It is almost time for dinner."

Molly told her parents about following Butch into the corn. Then she put her arm around me.

"I was scared stiff," Molly told them. "But Beth wasn't scared at all. Boy, does she have guts!"

Guts? Me? I couldn't believe my ears!

Dinner was great. We cooked hot dogs on sticks over a fire.

And there was plenty of corn on the cob.
"Oh, no! Not corn!" Molly and I shouted
together. But we each ate three ears anyway.

Right before bed I did get a little homesick. Molly's mom gave me a big hug. That helped.

Then Molly told me I was her best friend. We locked pinkies on it. That helped too.

Maybe Molly was right. Maybe I really am a kid with guts!

Molly the Brave and Me

Meet the Author

Jane O'Connor grew up on the west side of New York City. Since 1979 she has written many children's books, including a cookbook. She used her personal experiences at summer camp to write her first children's book, *Yours Till Niagara Falls, Abby.* She often works with other authors to write stories and nonfiction books.

Meet the Illustrator

Sheila Hamanaka would draw at the many museums she visited. Many ideas have come from memories of favorite places that she visited with her father. Her favorite subject to paint is people because there are so many different types. She likes to illustrate children's books because *"you can do anything you want, any subject."* She lives in the northern part of New York.

102

Theme Connections

Think About It

This story tells about courage from one point of view and how that view changes. Here are some questions to think about:

- What does the selection teach us about courage?
- Why was it important to Beth that Molly think she was brave?
- Why didn't Beth think she was brave?
- Beth did everything Molly did in the country. Why didn't Molly think Beth was brave until the very end?

Post any question you have about courage on the Concept/Question Board. As you read more stories in this unit, answer any questions you can.

Record Ideas

 Record in your Writing Journal any new ideas about Courage that you thought about or discussed with others.

Interview Questions

- Work with a partner and make a list of questions you would like to ask a brave person.
- Copy the list of questions on a piece of paper.
- Ask a friend or person you feel is brave the questions and record their answers.

Courage

Emily Hearn
illustrated by Bo-Kim Louie

Courage is when you're allergic to cats and

your new friend says can you come to her house to play after school and

stay to dinner then maybe go skating and sleep overnight? And,

she adds, you can pet her small kittens! Oh, how you ache to. It

takes courage to say "no" to all that.

Dragons
and
Giants

by Arnold Lobel

Frog and Toad were reading a book together. "The people in this book are brave," said Toad. "They fight dragons and giants, and they are never afraid."

"I wonder if we are brave," said Frog. Frog and Toad looked into a mirror.

"We look brave," said Frog.

"Yes, but are we?" asked Toad.

Frog and Toad went outside.

"We can try to climb this mountain," said
Frog. "That should tell us if we are brave."

Frog went leaping over rocks, and Toad
came puffing up behind him.

They came to a dark cave. A big snake
came out of the cave.

"Hello lunch," said the snake when he
saw Frog and Toad. He opened his wide
mouth. Frog and Toad jumped away. Toad
was shaking.

"I am not afraid!" he cried.

They climbed higher, and they heard a
loud noise. Many large stones were rolling
down the mountain.

"It's an avalanche!" cried Toad. Frog and
Toad jumped away. Frog was trembling.

"I am not afraid!" he shouted.

They came to the top of the mountain. The shadow of a hawk fell over them. Frog and Toad jumped under a rock. The hawk flew away.

"We are not afraid!" screamed Frog and Toad at the same time. Then they ran down the mountain very fast. They ran past the place where they saw the avalanche. They ran past the place where they saw the snake. They ran all the way to Toad's house.

"Frog, I am glad to have a brave friend
like you," said Toad. He jumped into the
bed and pulled the covers over his head.

"And I am happy to know a brave person like you, Toad," said Frog. He jumped into the closet and shut the door.

Toad stayed in the bed, and Frog stayed in the closet.

They stayed there for a long time, just feeling very brave together.

Dragons and Giants

Meet the Author and Illustrator

Arnold Lobel was not big and strong when he was a child. Sometimes the other children would tease him. He would often make up stories to protect himself from the bullies and to amuse his friends. This was good practice for his later career as an author and illustrator.

During summer vacations, he and his family spent time in Vermont. His children caught many frogs and toads. Sometimes they took them home to New York to keep as pets for the year. The following summer, they would return the creatures where they had found them. Arnold Lobel said, *"I loved those little creatures and I think they led to the creation of my two most famous characters, Frog and Toad."*

Theme Connections

Think About It

What did you learn about courage from "Dragons and Giants"? Here are some questions to discuss:

- Why did Frog and Toad decide to see if they are brave?
- What difference do you think it made that Toad and Frog were together?
- Do you think Frog and Toad proved that they are brave?

Check the Concept/Question Board and answer any questions you can. Post any new questions.

Record Ideas

In your Writing Journal, record your ideas about courage in short phrases, sentences, or in a chart.

Make Other Stories

Frog and Toad faced three dangers: the snake, the avalanche, and the hawk. Make another story showing courage following these steps:

- For each danger, make one box big enough to write a paragraph and draw a picture in.
- For each danger, write another brave way that Frog and Toad could have dealt with their fear.
- Draw a picture to go with the paragraph.

Life doesn't frighten me

Maya Angelou
Illustrated by Dara Goldman

Shadow on the wall
Noises down the hall
Life doesn't frighten me at all
Bad dogs barking loud
Big ghosts in a cloud
Life doesn't frighten me at all.

Mean old Mother Goose
Lions on the loose
They don't frighten me at all
Dragons breathing flame
On my counterpane
That doesn't frighten me at all.

I go boo
Make them shoo
I make fun
Way them run
I won't cry
So they fly
I just smile
They go wild
Life doesn't frighten me at all.

Tough guys in a fight
All alone at night
Life doesn't frighten me at all.
Panthers in the park
Strangers in the dark
No, they don't frighten me at all.

That new classroom where
Boys all pull my hair
(Kissy little girls
With their hair in curls)
They don't frighten me at all.

Don't show me frogs and snakes
And listen for my scream,
If I'm afraid at all
It's only in my dreams.

I've got a magic charm
That I keep up my sleeve,
I can walk the ocean floor
And never have to breathe.

Life doesn't frighten me at all
Not at all
Not at all
Life doesn't frighten me at all.

The Hole in the Dike

retold by Norma Green
illustrated by Eric Carle

A long time ago, a boy named Peter lived
in Holland. He lived with his mother and
father in a cottage next to a tulip field.
Peter loved to look at the old windmills
turning slowly.

118

He loved to look at the sea.

In Holland, the land is very low, and the
sea is very high. The land is kept safe and
dry by high, strong walls called dikes.

One day Peter went to visit a friend who lived by the seaside.

As he started for home, he saw that the sun was setting and the sky was growing dark. "I must hurry or I shall be late for supper," said Peter.

"Take the short-cut along the top of the dike," his friend said.

They waved good-bye.

Peter wheeled his bike to the road on top
of the dike. It had rained for several days,
and the water looked higher than usual.

Peter thought, "It's lucky that the dikes are
high and strong. Without these dikes, the land
would be flooded and everything would be
washed away."

121

Suddenly he heard a soft, gurgling noise.
He saw a small stream of water trickling
through a hole in the dike below.

Peter got off his bike to see what was wrong.

He couldn't believe his eyes. There in the
big strong dike was a leak!

Peter slid down to the bottom of the dike.
He put his finger in the hole to keep the
water from coming through.

He looked around for help, but he could
not see anyone on the road. He shouted.
Maybe someone in the nearby field would
hear him, he thought.

Only his echo answered. Everyone had
gone home.

Peter knew that if he let the water leak
through the hole in the dike, the hole would
get bigger and bigger. Then the sea would
come gushing through. The fields and the
houses and the windmills would all be flooded.

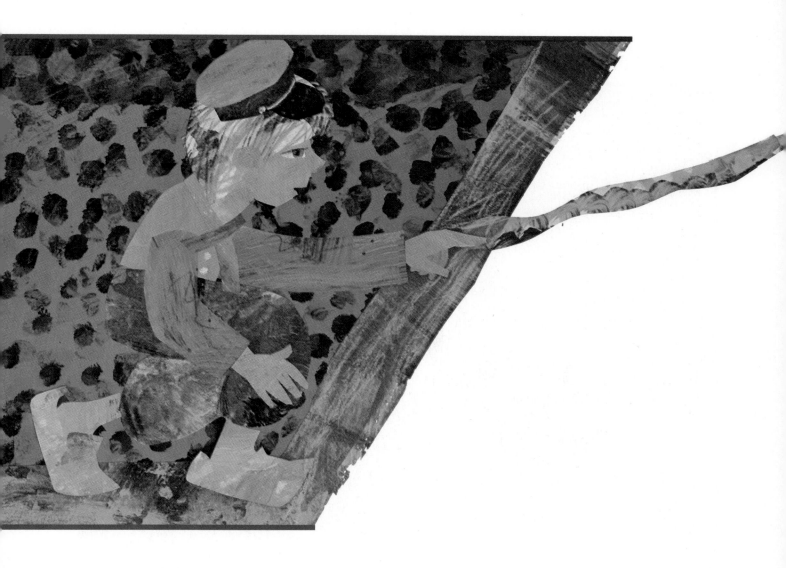

Peter looked around for something to plug up the leak so he could go to the village for help.

He put a stone in the hole, then a stick. But the stone and the stick were washed away by the water.

Peter had to stay there alone. He had to use all his strength to keep the water out.

From time to time he called for help. But no one heard him.

All night long Peter kept his finger in the dike.

His fingers grew cold and numb. He wanted to sleep, but he couldn't give up.

At last, early in the morning, Peter heard a welcome sound. Someone was coming! It was the milk cart rumbling down the road.

Peter shouted for help. The milkman was surprised to hear someone near that road so early in the morning. He stopped and looked around.

"Help!!" Peter shouted. "Here I am, at the bottom of the dike. There's a leak in the dike. Help! Help!"

The man saw Peter and hurried down to him. Peter showed him the leak and the little stream of water coming through.

Peter asked the milkman to hurry to the village. "Tell the people. Ask them to send some men to repair the dike right away!"

The milkman went as fast as he could. Peter had to stay with his finger in the dike.

At last the men from the village came. They set to work to repair the leak.

All the people thanked Peter. They carried him on their shoulders, shouting, "Make way for the hero of Holland! The brave boy who saved our land!"

But Peter did not think of himself as a hero. He had done what he thought was right. He was glad that he could do something for the country he loved so much.

131

The Hole in the Dike

Meet the Author

Norma Green says that more than a hundred years ago, an American woman named Mary Mapes Dodge told this story of the dike to her children, making it up as she went along. It was first published in her book *Hans Brinker or the Silver Skates*. The story became so famous that the Dutch people put up a statue of Peter in a little town called Spaarndam.

Green said, *"I felt there was a need today for young people to read about courage and pride in country. This story seemed to be a way of passing on these messages in a memorable fantasy."*

Meet the Illustrator

Eric Carle was born in New York. When he was six, his parents moved to Germany. After finishing art school in Germany, he moved back to the United States. He worked for a newspaper, the army, and an advertising agency before working as an illustrator full time. His books are often full of surprises. His books sometimes have pages with holes, flaps to look behind, uneven pages, and foldouts. He often hides the initials or names of his two children, Cirsten and Rolf, in his illustrations.

Theme Connections

Think About It

People can be heroes in many ways. Here are some questions to help you think about courage:

- Why was Peter considered a hero by others?
- Why didn't Peter consider himself a hero?
- Why do you think Peter chose to try and plug the dike himself rather than going to get help?
- What do you think was brave about what Peter did?

Check the Concept/Question Board and answer any questions you can. Post any new questions you have about Courage. The next story may answer the questions.

Record Ideas

Record in your Writing Journal the ideas that you thought about and talked about with others.

Make a New Ending

Write a new ending for the story.

- What might happen if Peter ran for help instead of plugging the hole in the dike?
- Would the dike burst before help could come?
- Would Peter still be considered brave and a hero by the people of his village?

FINE Art

Warrior Chief, warriors, and attendants. 16th–17th century. **Bini people, from the palace in Benin City, Nigeria.** Brass plaque. The Metropolitan Museum of Art, New York. Gift of Mr. and Mrs. Klaus G. Perls, 1990 (90.332). Photo: © 1998 The Metropolitan Museum of Art.

Lake Spirit. 1988. **Dale De Armond.** Wood engraving on paper. 6 × 5 in. The National Museum of Women in the Arts, Washington, D.C. Gift of the artist.

The Life-Line. 1884. **Winslow Homer.** Oil on canvas. The George W. Elkins Collection, Philadelphia Museum of Art.

A Picture Book of
Martin Luther King, Jr.

David A. Adler
illustrated by Robert Casilla

Martin Luther King, Jr. was one of
America's great leaders. He was a
powerful speaker, and he spoke out against
laws which kept black people out of many
schools and jobs. He led protests and
marches demanding fair laws for all people.

Martin Luther King, Jr. was born on January 15, 1929 in Atlanta, Georgia. Martin's father was a pastor. His mother had been a teacher. Martin had an older sister, Willie Christine, and a younger brother, Alfred Daniel.

Young Martin liked to play baseball, football, and basketball. He liked to ride his bicycle and to sing. He often sang in his father's church.

Martin (center) with his brother Alfred Daniel (left) and his sister Willie Christine (right)

Young Martin played in his backyard with his friends. One day he was told that two of his friends would no longer play with him, because they were white and he was black.

Martin cried. He didn't understand why the color of his skin should matter to anyone.

Martin's mother told him that many years ago black people were brought in chains to America and sold as slaves. She told him that long before Martin was born the slaves had been set free. However, there were still some people who did not treat black people fairly.

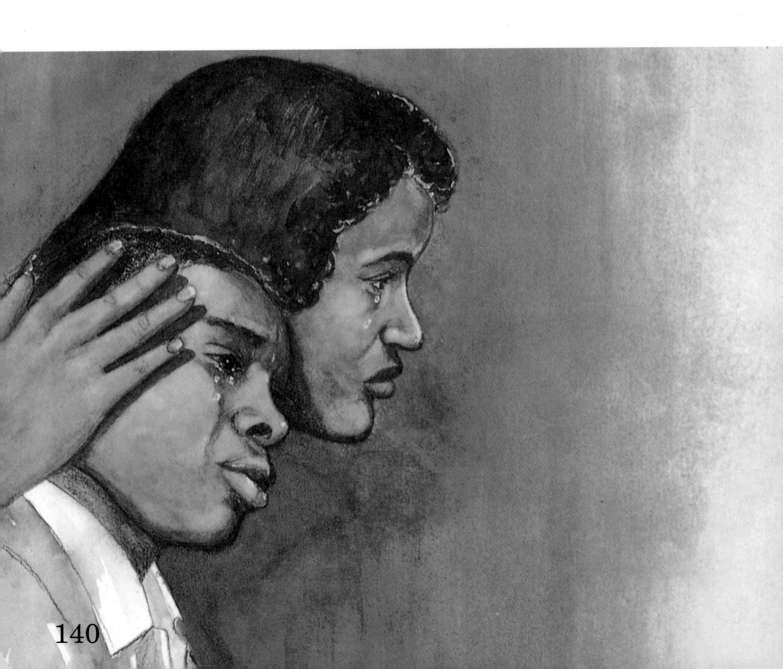

In Atlanta, where Martin lived, and elsewhere in the United States, there were "White Only" signs. Black people were not allowed in some parks, pools, hotels, restaurants and even schools. Blacks were kept out of many jobs.

Martin learned to read at home before he was old enough to start school. All through his childhood, he read books about black leaders.

Frederick Douglass

Harriet Tubman

George Washington Carver

Martin was a good student. He finished high school two years early and was just fifteen when he entered Morehouse College in Atlanta. At college Martin decided to become a minister.

After Martin was graduated from Morehouse, he studied for a doctorate at Boston University. While he was there he met Coretta Scott. She was studying music. They fell in love and married.

In 1954 Martin Luther King, Jr. began his first job as a pastor in Montgomery, Alabama. The next year Rosa Parks, a black woman, was arrested in Montgomery. She had been sitting just behind the "White Only" section on the bus. When all the seats in that section were taken, the driver told her to get up so a white man could have her seat. Rosa Parks refused.

Dr. Martin Luther King, Jr. led a protest. Blacks throughout the city refused to ride the buses. Dr. King said, "There comes a time when people get tired of being kicked about."

One night, while Dr. King was at a meeting, someone threw a bomb into his house.

Martin's followers were angry. They wanted to fight. Martin told them to go home peacefully. "We must love our white brothers," he said. "We must meet hate with love."

The bus protest lasted almost a year. When it ended there were no more "White Only" sections on buses.

Dr. King decided to move back to Atlanta in 1960. There, he continued to lead peaceful protests against "White Only" waiting rooms, lunch counters and rest rooms. He led many marches for freedom.

In 1963 Dr. King led the biggest march of all—the March on Washington. More than two hundred thousand black and white people followed him. "I have a dream," he said in his speech. "I have a dream that my four children will one day live in a nation where they will not be judged by the color of their skin but by the content of their character."

The next year in 1964, Dr. King was awarded one of the greatest honors any person can win, the Nobel Peace Prize.

The country was changing. New laws were passed. Blacks could go to the same schools as whites. They could go to the same stores, restaurants and hotels. "White Only" signs were against the law.

Dr. King told his followers to protest peacefully. But there were some riots and some violence.

Then, in April 1968, Dr. King went to Memphis, Tennessee. He planned to march so black and white garbage workers would get the same pay for the same work.

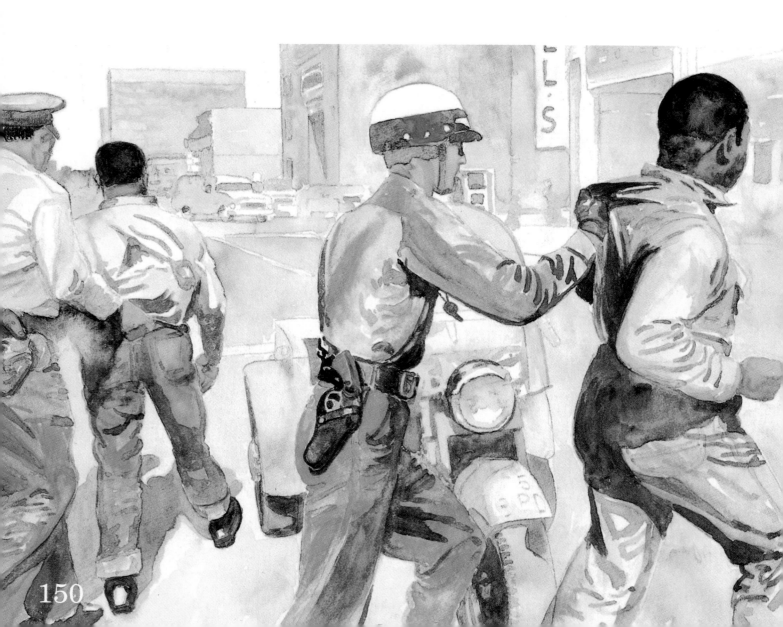

On April 4 in Memphis, Dr. King stood outside his motel room. Another man, James Earl Ray, was hiding nearby. He pointed a rifle at Dr. King. He fired the gun. An hour later Dr. King was dead.

Martin Luther King, Jr. dreamed of a world free of hate, prejudice and violence. Carved on the stone which marks his grave are the words, "I'm free at last."

A Picture Book of
Martin Luther King, Jr.

Meet the Author

David Adler's parents encouraged all six of their children to read and develop their own talents. He was known for his artistic ability and he would often tell stories to his brothers and sisters.

He was a math teacher, a cartoonist, and an arts and crafts teacher before he became a writer. He wrote his first children's book while he was a math teacher. By watching and listening to other people, he gets many ideas for his stories.

Meet the Illustrator

Robert Casilla was born in Jersey City, New Jersey. He began illustrating after graduating from the School of Visual Arts. He said, *"I find great rewards and satisfaction in illustrating for children."*

He has illustrated ten other biographies written by David Adler. When he illustrates a biography, he first tries to learn a lot about the person. Knowing the person very well helps him when he works on the art.

Theme Connections

Think About It

Martin Luther King, Jr. showed personal courage. Here are some questions to think about:

- What did Martin Luther King, Jr. do in his life that was brave?
- Why was Martin Luther King, Jr. willing to put himself in danger to help others?

Check the Concept/Question Board and answer any questions you can. Post any new questions you have about courage.

Record Ideas

 In your Writing Journal list your ideas or present them in a chart form.

Make a Diagram

Make two big boxes with enough room between them to write short sentences. In the left-hand box, write the main problem that was facing Martin Luther King, Jr. In the right-hand box, write what his idea was for confronting the problem. On the lines between the boxes, write events that occurred to make Martin Luther King, Jr. determined to carry out his idea. Your diagram should look similar to this:

Problem:

1. Laws kept African Americans from many jobs and schools.

2.

Idea:

The Empty Pot

by Demi

A long time ago in China there was a boy named Ping who loved flowers. Anything he planted burst into bloom. Up came flowers, bushes, and even big fruit trees, as if by magic!

Everyone in the kingdom loved flowers too. They planted them everywhere, and the air smelled like perfume.

The Emperor loved birds and animals, but flowers most of all, and he tended his own garden every day. But the Emperor was very old. He needed to choose a successor to the throne.

Who would his successor be? And how would the Emperor choose? Because the Emperor loved flowers so much, he decided to let the flowers choose.

The next day a proclamation was issued: All the children in the land were to come to the palace. There they would be given special flower seeds by the Emperor. "Whoever can show me their best in a year's time," he said, "will succeed me to the throne."

This news created great excitement throughout the land! Children from all over the country swarmed to the palace to get their flower seeds. All the parents wanted their children to be chosen Emperor, and all the children hoped they would be chosen too!

When Ping received his seed from the Emperor, he was the happiest child of all. He was sure he could grow the most beautiful flower.

Ping filled a flowerpot with rich soil. He planted the seed in it very carefully.

He watered it every day. He couldn't wait to see it sprout, grow, and blossom into a beautiful flower!

Day after day passed, but nothing grew in his pot.

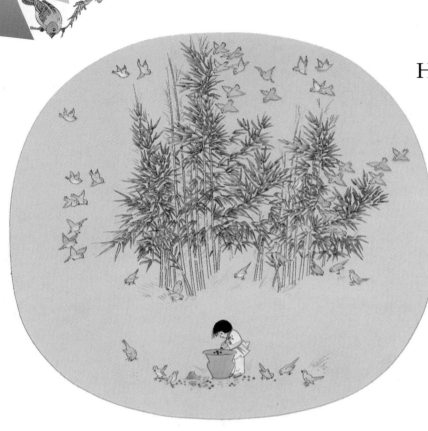

Ping was very worried. He put new soil into a bigger pot. Then he transferred the seed into the rich black soil.

Another two months he waited. Still nothing happened.

By and by the whole year passed.

Spring came, and all the children put on their best clothes to greet the Emperor.

They rushed to the palace with their beautiful flowers, eagerly hoping to be chosen.

Ping was ashamed of his empty pot. He thought the other children would laugh at him because for once he couldn't get a flower to grow.

His clever friend ran by, holding a great big plant. "Ping!" he said. "You're not really going to the Emperor with an empty pot, are you? Couldn't you grow a great big flower like mine?"

"I've grown lots of flowers better than yours," Ping said. "It's just this seed that won't grow."

Ping's father overheard this and said, "You did your best, and your best is good enough to present to the Emperor."

Holding the empty pot in his hands, Ping went straight away to the palace.

The Emperor was looking at the flowers slowly, one by one.

How beautiful all the flowers were!

But the Emperor was frowning and did not say a word.

Finally he came to Ping. Ping hung his head in shame, expecting to be punished.

The Emperor asked him, "Why did you bring an empty pot?"

Ping started to cry and replied, "I planted the seed you gave me and I watered it every day, but it didn't sprout. I put it in a better pot with better soil, but still it didn't sprout! I tended it all year long, but nothing grew. So today I had to bring an empty pot without a flower. It was the best I could do."

When the Emperor heard these words, a smile slowly spread over his face, and he put his arm around Ping. Then he exclaimed to one and all, "I have found him! I have found the one person worthy of being Emperor!

"Where you got your seeds from, I do not know. For the seeds I gave you had all been cooked. So it was impossible for any of them to grow.

"I admire Ping's great courage to appear before me with the empty truth, and now I reward him with my entire kingdom and make him Emperor of all the land!"

The Empty Pot

Meet the Author and Illustrator

Charlotte Dumaresq Hunt uses her childhood nickname, Demi, as her pen name. She studied art in several schools, but much of her learning took place as she traveled. She has been to faraway places such as Brazil, India, and China. Some of the things she learned and saw while in China are seen in "The Empty Pot."

She has not limited her art to children's books. Many of her paintings and prints hang in museums in the United States and India. She has also painted wall murals in Mexico and the dome of a church in California.

Theme Connections

Think About It

"The Empty Pot" tells about a different type of courage. Here are some questions to think about:

- What did you expect Ping to do once he realized his seed would not grow? Why?
- Were you surprised by the ending? Why?
- What does the selection teach us about telling the truth and about courage?

Post any new questions you have about courage on the Concept/Question Board. The next story may answer the questions.

Record Ideas

Record in your Writing Journal the ideas that you thought about and talked about with others.

Make a Wheel of Emotions

- Draw a wheel on a piece of paper. Make enough space between the spokes to write on them.
- On each spoke write down the emotions that Ping experienced throughout the story and why you think he felt that way. For example, at the beginning of the story Ping is happy because he believes he can grow the best flower. Write that emotion on the first spoke.
- Complete your wheel by filling in the spokes with the different emotions that Ping had.

Brave as a Mountain Lion

Ann Herbert Scott
illustrated by Glo Coalson

It was snowing hard. Pressing his face against the cold glass of the living room window, Spider could barely see his father's horses crowding against the fence. Soon the reservation would be covered with darkness.

Spider shivered. Any other night he would have been hoping his father would reach home before the snow drifted too high to push through. But tonight was different. Tonight he dreaded his father's coming.

In his pocket Spider could feel two pieces of paper from school. One he wanted to show his father. One he didn't. Not tonight. Not ever.

Beside him on the couch his sister Winona was playing with her doll. Lucky kid, thought Spider. Winona was too little to worry about anything, especially school.

Just then Spider saw the blinking red lights of the snowplow clearing the road beside their house. Right behind came his father's new blue pickup. Spider sighed. At least Dad was home safe. Now the trouble would begin!

Winona ran to the back door. But Spider stayed on the couch, waiting. From the kitchen he could smell dinner cooking. His favorite, deer meat. But tonight he didn't even feel like eating. Soon he heard the sound of his father and his brother Will stomping the snow from their boots.

Spider's father came in with an armful of mail from the post office. He hung up his hat and jacket on the pegs by the kitchen and stretched out in his favorite chair.

"So what did you do in school today?" he asked Spider.

"Not much," said Spider, feeling his pocket.

"Did you bring home any papers?"

Spider nodded. How did his father always know?

"Let's take a look," said his father.

Spider took the first paper from his pocket. "Here's the good one," he said.

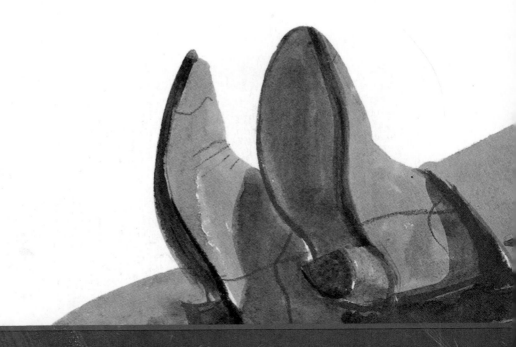

"Spelling one hundred percent. Every word correct. Good for you, son."

"But, Dad, I'm in trouble." Spider shoved the other paper into his father's hand. "The teacher wants me to be in the big school spelling bee."

Spider's father read out loud: "Dear Parent, I am pleased to inform you that your son Spider has qualified for the school spelling bee, which will be held next Thursday night. We hope you and your family will attend."

Spider's mother and grandmother came in from the kitchen with the platter of deer meat and bowls of beans and corn for dinner. "That's a good report, Little Brother," his grandmother said, smiling.

"But I won't do it," said Spider.

"Why not?" asked Will.

"I'm too afraid," said Spider.

"But you're a brave boy," said his father. "Why are you afraid?"

"Dad," said Spider, "you have to stand high up on the stage in the gym and all the people look at you. I'm afraid my legs would freeze together and I wouldn't be able to walk. And if I did get up there, no sound would come out when I opened my mouth. It's too scary."

"Oh, I see," said his father.

Spider's mother put her hand on his shoulder. "You must be hungry. Let's eat."

After dinner Spider sat by the wood stove doing his homework. "Dad, were you ever in a spelling bee?" he asked.

"As a matter of fact, I was."

"Were you scared?"

"I was very scared. I didn't even want to do it. But then my father told me to pretend I was a brave animal, the strongest, bravest animal I could think of. Then I wasn't afraid anymore."

Later, Spider sat up in bed thinking of animals who weren't afraid of anything. Above his head hung the picture of a mountain lion his dad had painted for him. How about a mountain lion, the King of the Beasts?

Spider took his flashlight from under his pillow and shined its beam on the face of the great wild creature. "Brave as a mountain lion," he said to himself in a loud, strong voice.

"Brave as a mountain lion," he repeated in his mind as he was falling asleep.

"I'll try to be brave as a mountain lion," he whispered to his father the next morning as he brushed his hair for school.

At recess the next day Spider peeked into the gymnasium. The huge room was empty. He looked up at the mural painting of the western Shoshone people of long ago. They were brave hunters of deer and antelope and elk, just as his father and his uncles were today.

At the far end of the gym was the scoreboard with the school's emblem, the eagle. Every Saturday in the winter Spider and his whole family came to cheer for Will and the basketball team. Those players weren't afraid of anything.

Then Spider stared up at the stage. That's where the spellers would stand. He could feel his throat tighten and hear his heart thumping, bumpity-bumpity-bumpity-bump. How could he ever get up there in front of all the people? Spider ran outside, slamming the gym door behind him.

That afternoon it was still snowing. At home Spider found his grandmother beading a hatband for his father's birthday. Spider watched her dip her needle into the bowls of red and black and white beads.

"Grandma, were you ever in a spelling bee?"

"No, I never was," his grandmother answered. "Are you thinking much about it?"

"All the time," said Spider.

"What's the worst part?"

"Being up on the stage with all the people looking at you."

"Oh, that's easy," said his grandmother. "You can be clever. Clever as a coyote. The coyote always has some trick to help him out of trouble. When you're up there on the stage, you don't have to look at the people. You can turn your back on them and pretend they aren't even there."

In bed that night Spider pulled the covers over his head. "Brave as a mountain lion, clever as a coyote," he kept repeating to himself as he fell asleep.

The next morning Spider scraped a peephole in the ice on his bedroom window. He couldn't see the far mountains for the swirling snow. He smiled as he packed his book bag. If it kept snowing like this, maybe the principal would close school tomorrow.

In class that day all everybody could talk about was the spelling bee. "Can we count on you, Spider?" asked Miss Phillips, his teacher.

Spider shook his head. "Maybe," he said. "I haven't made up my mind."

"You'd better make up your mind soon," said Miss Phillips. "The spelling bee is tomorrow night."

After lunch Spider walked by the gym door, but this time he didn't open it. He didn't have to. He remembered just how everything looked. Scary. When he thought about it, a shiver went all the way down his spine.

By the afternoon the snow had piled in drifts higher than Spider's head. Spider got a bowl of popcorn and went to the carport to watch Will shoot baskets. Time after time the ball slipped through the net. Will almost never missed.

"How about some popcorn for me?" Will asked his little brother. Spider brought back another bowl from the kitchen.

"Are you practicing for the spelling bee?" asked Will.

"I've decided not to be in it," said Spider. "I'm going to be brave when I'm bigger."

Will nodded. "I remember those spelling bees."

"Were you afraid?" asked Spider.

"I was scared silly," said Will. "I was so scared I was afraid I'd wet my pants. Then I learned the secret."

"What's the secret?" asked Spider.

"To be silent."

"Silent?" asked Spider. "What does that do?"

"It keeps you cool. When I have a hard shot to make and the whole team depends on me, that's when I get very silent."

Spider didn't say anything. He just watched his brother shooting one basket after another. Then he saw her. High above the shelves of paint and livestock medicines was a tiny insect. It was his old friend, Little Spider, dangling on a long strand as she spun a new part of her web. She was silent. Silent as the moon.

Spider laughed. How could he have forgotten! Grandmother often told him how when he was a baby in his cradle board he used to watch for hours while a little spider spun her web above his head. She had been his first friend. Ever since, his family had called him Spider.

Taking the stepladder, Spider climbed up close so he could watch the tiny creature. How brave she was, dropping down into space with nothing to hang onto. And how clever, weaving a web out of nothing but her own secret self. "Say something," he whispered.

The little insect was silent. But Spider felt she was talking to him in her own mysterious way. "Listen to your spirit," she seemed to say. "Listen to your spirit and you'll never be afraid."

The next morning the snow had stopped. Outside Spider's window icicles glistened in the sun. No chance of school being closed today.

"Brave as a mountain lion, clever as a coyote, silent as a spider," Spider thought to himself as he buttoned his vest.

Winona pushed open the door. "Are you going to do it?"

"I'm going to do it," Spider answered.

That night all the family came, his grandmother who lived with them and his other grandparents and his father and his mother and three aunts and two uncles and Will and Winona and lots of their cousins. Three of his cousins were going to be in the spelling bee, too.

Brave as a mountain lion, Spider climbed up the steps to the stage. Clever as a coyote, he turned his back so he wouldn't see the rows of people down below. Silently, he listened to his spirit. Bumpity-bump-bump went his heart.

All the best spellers in his class were up there on the stage, standing in a line. The principal gave them the words, one by one.

At first the words were easy. "Yellow," said the principal. "I have a yellow dog."

Spider kept his eyes on the principal's face. "Yellow," said Spider. "Y-e-l-l-o-w. Yellow."

"Correct," said the principal.

Then the words got a little harder. "February," said the principal. "Soon it will be February." It was Spider's turn again.

"February," said Spider, remembering the *r*. "Capital f-e-b-r-u-a-r-y. February."

"Correct," said the principal.

Finally there were only two spellers left standing—Spider and Elsie, a girl from the other side of the reservation.

"Terrific," said the principal. "We have a terrific basketball team."

"Terrific," said Spider, taking a big breath. "T-e-r-r-i-f-f-i-c. Terrific."

"Incorrect," said the principal. Then she turned to Elsie. "Terrific. We have a terrific basketball team."

"Terrific," said Elsie. "T-e-r-r-i-f-i-c. Terrific."

"Correct," said the principal. "Let's give a hand to our two winners from Miss Phillips' class: Elsie in first place and Spider in second place."

It was over! Spider climbed down the steps and found the rows where his family were sitting. Spider's father shook his hand and Will slapped him on the back. "You did it!" his mother said proudly. "You stood right up there in front of everybody!"

"It was easy," said Spider.

"You were brave," said his father. "Brave as a mountain lion."

"And clever," said his grandmother. "Clever as a coyote."

I wasn't even afraid, Spider thought. I listened to my spirit. "But now I'm hungry," he told his family. "Hungry as a bear. Let's all go home and eat."

Brave as a Mountain Lion

Meet the Author

Ann Herbert Scott often becomes familiar with the people and places she writes about. As she writes, she pictures each scene in her mind. She also talks a lot with children to see what they think about her ideas. When speaking about this story, she said, *"The story idea came directly from a boy who was confronted by an everyday challenge to his courage: his fear of standing up before an audience as part of the annual school spelling bee."*

Meet the Illustrator

Glo Coalson has always loved art and the out-of-doors. After a friend suggested that she illustrate books, she wrote and illustrated her first book. It was created from Eskimo folktales that she had collected while in Alaska. Since then, she has illustrated over 20 children's books. She uses watercolor, pastels, and ink to create her illustrations.

Theme Connections

Think About It

Here are some questions to think about:

- Why was Spider afraid of being in the spelling bee?
- How was Spider able to overcome his fear of being in the spelling bee?
- What does the story teach us about courage?

Check the Concept/Question Board and answer any questions you can.

Record Ideas

Record in your Writing Journal the ideas that you thought about and talked about with others.

Make a Goals Thermometer

- Draw a large thermometer to measure Spider's level of courage. Write "No courage" at the bottom and "In the spelling bee" at the top.
- On the first line above "No courage," write the first thing Spider did to build his courage. Color in that amount of courage.
- Continue to write ways that Spider built his courage and to color in the thermometer.
- Your thermometer might look like this:

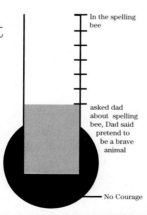

In the spelling bee

asked dad about spelling bee, Dad said pretend to be a brave animal

No Courage

Bibliography

Arnie and the Skateboard Gang

by **Nancy Carlson.** Is it braver to say no or skateboard down Hairy Kerry Hill? See what Arnie decides.

Brave Horace

by **Holly Keller.** How does Horace find the nerve to go to a monster-movie party? Would you be scared?

Fabulous Flying Fandinis

by **Ingrid Snyder.** Fandini family fun: trapezes, trampolines and unicycles. How does Bobby find the courage to share in their adventures?

Faraway Drums

by **Virginia Kroll.** Which is scarier: city noises or jungle noises? Read how Jamila deals with her fear.

Fly Away Home

by Eve Bunting. With no home but the airport, Andrew and his father bravely face each day. Read about their special kind of courage.

Harry and the Terrible Whatzit

by Dick Gackenbach. Is the terrible whatzit in the cellar as bad as Harry thinks it is? He's about to find out as he goes in search of his mother.

Shy Charles

by Rosemary Wells. No talk but all action. Silent Charles may surpise you!

What's Under My Bed?

by James Stevenson. Louie and Mary discover that Grandpa, too, was afraid of things under his bed. What are those things anyway?

Many people in this country came from faraway countries to live here. Where did they come from? Why did they come? Did your family come from far away? Meet some of these people and find out their stories.

Immigrants: Coming to America

from *You Are There: Immigrants Coming to America*
by Gare Thompson

Immigrants

North America is made up of many peoples. All of them came from other places—willingly or unwillingly. People coming from other places are called immigrants. The immigrants to North America came from Europe, Asia, Africa, and Central and South America. They came to try to make a better life.

Strangers in a Strange Land

The First Immigrants

The very first immigrants were American Indians. They may have come across a land bridge from Asia to Alaska. Then they slowly moved south. Others may have come across oceans in small boats.

American Indians in canoes

The Search for Riches

Explorers from many different countries were the next group to come to America. They were looking for riches. Christopher Columbus opened up America for future immigrants. He was an Italian sailor exploring for Spain. He first arrived in the Americas in 1492. His writings about the New World made others want to go there.

Columbus landing in the New World

The Real Riches: Land

Most explorers were looking for gold. They found none. The real riches in America were its land. The forests were filled with birds and animals. Fruits and grains grew wild. The sea, lakes, and rivers held fish.

America's rich land

Escape to America

There were many reasons why people came to America in the early 1600s. England had too many people. Work was hard to get. Sickness and hunger were common. Some people were not allowed to practice their religion.

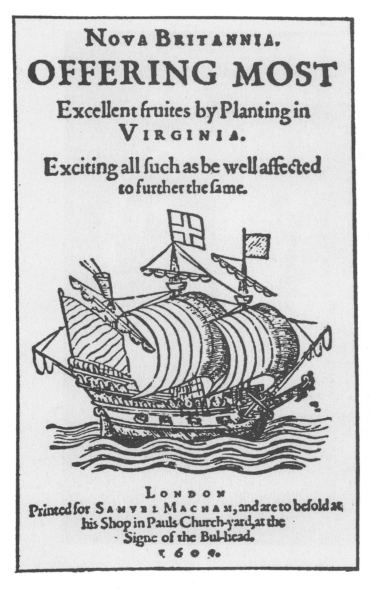

Nova Britannia.

OFFERING MOST

Excellent fruites by Planting in
VIRGINIA.

Exciting all such as be well affected
to further the same.

LONDON
Printed for Samvel Machan, and are to be sold at
his Shop in Pauls Church-yard, at the
Signe of the Bul-head.
1609.

Land for sale in the New World

The First Settlement

The first settlement in America was Jamestown, Virginia. It was founded in 1607. Its settlers were not hard workers. They refused to raise food, build, or do any other hard work. The colony's leader, Captain John Smith, finally ordered them to "work or starve." After that, everyone worked.

The first settlement at Jamestown

The Pilgrims

In the late summer of 1620, a group of Pilgrims set sail for America on their ship *Mayflower*. They left England for religious freedom and a better life. The trip took 66 days. Their new colony in Massachusetts was called Plimoth.

The Mayflower

Learning About the New Land

Native Americans taught the early settlers how to live in America. They taught them which animals were best to eat, what foods grew well, how to make canoes and moccasins, and much more.

Did You Know?

The Native Americans gave the settlers many new foods. These included corn, potatoes, peanuts, squashes, peppers, tomatoes, and pumpkins.

Explorers meet the Native Americans

Against Their Will

Most people came to America with hopes for a better life. But Africans left their homes against their will. For them life in America meant the end of freedom and hope for the future.

Captured Africans

First Servants, Then Slaves

The first group of Africans were brought to Jamestown in 1619. They were not slaves but indentured servants. They had signed contracts to work for seven years. Then they were free. White immigrants worked as indentured servants, too. After 1660, African-Americans were slaves.

Africans landing at Jamestown

Settling a New Country 1620–1776

By 1750 new immigrants to America found cities, newspapers, schools, churches, roads, and stores. These new settlers included Irish, Jewish, Swedish, African, Dutch, German, French, and Polish. Each group brought its own foods, ways of worship, art, music, holidays, language, and habits.

Settlers from Around the World

Dutch Settlers

In 1621 the Dutch set up a colony they called New Netherland. Its capital was New Amsterdam. Cozy tile-roofed houses lined its narrow streets. Within a few years more than a dozen languages could be heard on its busy streets. In 1664 the British captured New Amsterdam and renamed it New York.

New Amsterdam

Jewish Settlers

The first Jewish settlers in North America were twenty-three people who settled in New Amsterdam in 1654. The governor of new Amsterdam, Peter Stuyvesant, welcomed them. Their families became well-known merchants. They bought and sold goods all over the world.

Peter Stuyvesant

German Settlers

In 1683 a small group of Germans founded the town of Germantown in Philadelphia, Pennsylvania. The Germans were excellent farmers. Their ways of planting different crops every year and using fertilizer are still used today.

The Germans in Pennsylvania were called Pennsylvania Dutch for "Deutsch," meaning German. They were known for their handsome folk art.

This Pennsylvania Dutch chest held linens.

Women Settlers

Fewer women than men came to the New World in the early years. But those who did come worked very hard. They cared for their families and their homes.

But they also taught the children, farmed the fields, and cared for the animals. Some women settlers became doctors, printers, and poets. Phillis Wheatley, an enslaved woman, published a book of poems when she was 19.

Phillis Wheatley

Enslaved African-Americans

By 1775 about half a million African-Americans were living in America. Most were enslaved and most lived in the South. Many were experienced farmers and fine fishermen. Their earlier life in Africa had taught them how to live in a hot, humid climate. They made farming in the South successful.

African-Americans farming

Teaching the Settlers Farming

Africans taught the English colonists how to grow rice. Rice is a basic crop in parts of Africa. It grew well in swampy areas such as South Carolina.

Rice harvesting

Rice

No Longer Just English

The American colonies were ruled by Great Britain. But colonists came from many other countries. No matter where they came from, most colonists were unhappy with British rule. They felt many British laws were unfair. A revolution was coming!

Their New Country

The Revolution was won with the help of many foreign-born people. One was Baron von Steuben, a German noble, who trained the colonial army. The important role these people played helped them win the rights of citizens. The new United States of America would continue to welcome immigrants.

Baron von Steuben training the colonial army

Still Coming Today
1945 to Today

The United States continues to welcome immigrants in modern times. Most are from Asia, Africa, Central and South America, and the Caribbean.

The reasons people come here have not changed. They come to find work, to educate their children, and to live better.

The United States gains from the work immigrants do. And everyone is made richer by celebrating so many different ways of life.

Enriching America

Spanish Immigrants

Many immigrants have come to the United States from Spanish-speaking countries. The Spanish language and Spanish culture are very important in American life.

A cafe in Little Havana, Miami

From Mexico to the United States

Since the early 1900s many Mexicans have come to the United States. They too are looking for higher-paying jobs and the chance for a better life.

Mexican-American girls celebrating Independence Day, Chicago

From the Islands

People from the Caribbean island countries have come to the United States in large numbers in recent years. Most of them have settled in cities, especially New York and Washington D.C. Some have started their own small businesses, especially restaurants and food stores.

From Cuba

Nearly 1 million Cuban Americans live in the United States today. Most of them came to this country in the early 1960s. They were not happy with the Cuban government. Most chose to live in Miami, Florida. Miami became the gateway to Central and South America.

Cubans arriving in the United States

From Asia

In the early 1990s about half of all immigrants entering the United States each year were Asian. Asian Americans are the fastest-growing group in the United States. They include people from China, Japan, Korea, the Philippines, India, and Southeast Asia.

Lab technician

Doctor

School children

Immigrants: Coming to America

Meet the Author

Gare Thompson decided to write "Immigrants: Coming to America" because children love to learn how people lived long ago. This story involved a lot of research. He read many stories, diaries, and letters, and visited many museums. Often he would change the story because he found a wonderful photo that would tell the story itself.

Before he wrote children's books, he started as a kindergarten teacher and later taught other grade levels. He has said, *"I think that it is important to get children writing as soon as possible. All children have a story to tell and it is our job to help them tell their stories."*

Theme Connections

Think About It

The United States of America is made of people who have come from many different places. Here are some questions to think about and discuss:

- What does "Immigrants: Coming to America" teach us about immigration and the people of our country?
- How are people coming to America the same? How are they different?

Post any questions you have about Our Country and Its People on the Concept/Question Board.

Record Ideas

In your Writing Journal, record how people that make up our country are the same and different.

Make a Time Line

Make a time line showing when different groups of people came to America.

- Draw a long line on a page in your Writing Journal.
- Place one dot along the line for each group that came to America.
- Label the dots with the group, the country that the group came from, and the year that they came in order from the earliest to the most recent.

Dreamplace

George Ella Lyon  *illustrated by Peter Catalanotto*

We drive up a steep road,
hike a paved trail
among yucca, pinyon, juniper
and tourists.

It's all plain as beans
till we come around a bend
and see for the first time
across the trees:
like a dream, like a sandcastle
this city the Pueblo people
built under a cliff.

238

Towers and courtyards,
hearths and kivas
hung where the eagle nests.

A sandcastle, but no water—
every drop carried down from mesa
or up from canyon
to this place
where the Anasazi
                    sang
                        and danced
                            and prayed
plaited sandals, wove baskets,
coiled clay into pots.

Food, too,
had to be grown above them
or hunted below them
harvest and kill
borne home on their backs
                    hands
                            and
feet
            finding
slots
            in the
stone.

In the courtyards, they took *mano,*
rounded pounding stones,
and crushed the corn into meal
on flat stones, *metate,*
and fed their families for a hundred years
as evening stretched its hand
                    over the mesa
and bathed their dwelling for a moment
in pink light.

Then
water dried up
corn withered
sickness came.

They packed their prayer sticks
and grinding stones
climbed down the cliff face
and set off leaving us
far in the future
to drive up roads they never knew
and hike trails to their city
and stand amazed

at the people
who built this dream
who lit its walls
with fire and stories
and then one day
when even trees were hungry
turned their backs

           and let it go.

Dreamplace

Meet the Author

George Ella Lyon wanted to be a vet, a singer, a translator, a neon sign maker, and a tightrope walker. Through writing, Lyon found that she could be all the things she wanted to be. When she visits classrooms, children ask her if she is rich. Her response is *"Yes, I say, but not the way you think. I'm rich because I get to do what I love to do. . . . So when kids are excited because they're meeting a 'real author,' I'm excited at meeting real readers."*

Meet the Illustrator

Peter Catalanotto says he has always been an artist. He was surprised when he started school and found that not everyone liked to draw. His favorite things to draw when he was young were comic book characters.

He illustrated over one hundred and fifty book jackets before he started to illustrate entire books. He has also written children's books. When he talks to children, he tells them *"to write about what they wished would happen to them along with what really does."*

Theme Connections

Think About It

Here are some questions to help you think about "Dreamplace":

- Why was a mix of rainy and sunny days important to the people in the story?
- Why did the Anasazi migrate from their home?
- How do we know about the lives of Pueblo people?

Check the Concept/Question Board and answer any questions you can. Post any new questions you have about Our Country and Its People.

Record Ideas

 Record in your Writing Journal the ideas that you thought about and talked about with others.

Make a Flow Chart

A flow chart is one way of showing how something changes over time. Make a flow chart to show what happened to the Anasazi people.

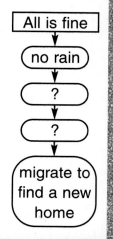

- Begin your flow chart with "All is fine." Then add events that caused change beginning with "No rain."
- Add what will happen if there is no rain for a long time and continue. Your flow chart can be as long as you can make it. It might look like this:

All is fine
↓
no rain
↓
?
↓
?
↓
migrate to find a new home

A Place Called Freedom

Scott Russell Sanders
illustrated by Thomas B. Allen

Down in Tennessee, on the plantation where I was born, Mama worked in the big house and Papa worked in the fields. The master of that big house set us free in the spring of 1832, when I was seven years old and my sister, Lettie, was five.

Papa called Lettie a short drink of water, because she was little and wriggly, and he called me a long gulp of air, because I was tall and full of talk.

As soon as we could pack some food and clothes, we left the plantation, heading north for Indiana. Our aunts and uncles and cousins who were still slaves hugged us hard and waved until we were out of sight.

Papa said it would be safer to travel at night.

"How're we going to find our way in the dark?" I asked him.

"We'll follow the drinking gourd," Papa answered. He pointed to the glittery sky, and I saw he meant the Big Dipper. He showed me how to find the North Star by drawing an arrow from the dipper's lip. Papa loved stars. That's why, when he gave up his old slave's name and chose a new one, he called himself Joshua Starman. And that's why my name is James Starman.

It was a weary, long way. Night after night as we traveled, the buttery bowl of the moon filled up, then emptied again. When Lettie got tired, she rode on Papa's shoulders for a while, or on Mama's hip. But I walked the whole way on my own feet.

At last one morning, just after sunrise, we came to the Ohio River. A fisherman with a face as wrinkled as an old boot carried us over the water in his boat. On the far shore we set our feet on the free soil of Indiana. White flowers covered the hills that day like feathers on a goose.

By and by we met a Quaker family who took us into their house, gave us seed, and loaned us a mule and a plow, all because they believed that slavery was a sin. We helped on their farm, working shoulder to shoulder, and we planted our own crops.

That first year Papa raised enough corn and wheat for us to buy some land beside the Wabash River, where the dirt was as black as my skin. Papa could grow anything, he could handle horses, and he could build a barn or a bed.

Before winter, Papa and Mama built us a sturdy cabin. Every night we sat by the fire and Papa told stories that made the shadows dance. Every morning Mama held school for Lettie and me. Mama knew how to read and write from helping with lessons for the master's children. She could sew clothes that fit you like the wind, and her cooking made your tongue glad.

While the ground was still frozen, Papa rode south through the cold nights, down to the plantation in Tennessee. We fretted until he showed up again at our door, leading two of my aunts, two uncles, and five cousins. They stayed with us until they could buy land near ours and build their own cabins.

Again and again Papa went back to Tennessee, and each time he came home with more of the folks we loved.

Hearing about our settlement, black people arrived from all over the South, some of them freed like us, some of them runaways. There were carpenters and blacksmiths, basket weavers and barrel makers.

Soon we had a church, then a store, then a stable, then a mill to grind our grain. For the first time in our lives, we had money, just enough to get by, and we watched every penny.

After a few years, the railroad decided to run tracks through our village, because so many people had gathered here. If our place was going to be on the map, it needed a name. At a meeting, folks said we should call it Starman, in honor of Mama and Papa. But Mama and Papa said, "No, let's name it Freedom."

And that's how we came to live in a place called Freedom.

We all celebrated the new name by building a school, where Mama could teach everyone, young and old, to read and write and do sums. She made me want to learn everything there was to know.

When Mama first told me about the alphabet, I wondered how I could ever remember twenty-six different letters. But I learned them all in a flash. It was like magic to me, the way those letters joined up to make words.

Papa's farming was also like magic. He would put seeds in the ground, and before you knew it, here came melon vines or cornstalks. He planted trees, and here came apples or nuts or shade.

For a long while, I couldn't decide whether I wanted to grow up and become a farmer like Papa or a teacher like Mama.

"I don't see why a teacher can't farm," Mama said.

"I don't see why a farmer can't teach," said Papa.

They were right, you know, because I raised the beans and potatoes for supper, and I wrote these words with my own hand.

A Place Called Freedom

Meet the Author

Scott Sanders has written realistic fiction, science fiction, folktales, and stories for children. In his work, he likes to ask questions that scientists might ask. He is concerned about people and how they solve their problems. Many of his writings are about the lives of rural people, children, and the elderly. He said, *"If my writing does not help my neighbors to live more alertly, pleasurably, or wisely, then it is worth little."*

Meet the Illustrator

Thomas B. Allen was born in Tennessee and took his first art class when he was nine-years old. His illustrations have appeared in many magazines and over twenty children's books. He tries to combine a feeling of the old and new in his pictures. In addition to painting, he enjoys using a pen-and-ink cross-hatching method.

Theme Connections

Think About It

Here are some questions to help you think about "A Place Called Freedom":

- Why is this story important for understanding the way in which people build lives better than the ones they leave?
- How did the people who joined the family contribute to the new town?
- What does the selection teach us about opportunities and following dreams?

Check the Concept/Question Board and answer any questions you can. Post any new questions.

Record Ideas

Record in your Writing Journal the ideas that you thought about. You may choose to simply list your ideas or to present them in a chart.

Make a Questionnaire

Think of at least five questions you would like to ask one of the characters in the story and write them down in your Writing Journal.

- Have a friend or someone at home ask you the questions.
- Answer the questions, pretending that you are the character in the story.
- Then write the answers in your journal.

The Story of the Statue of Liberty

Betsy Maestro
illustrated by Giulio Maestro

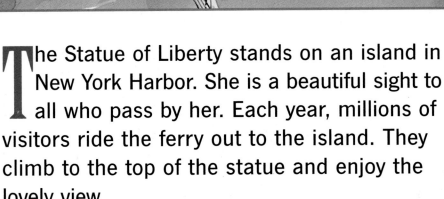

The Statue of Liberty stands on an island in New York Harbor. She is a beautiful sight to all who pass by her. Each year, millions of visitors ride the ferry out to the island. They climb to the top of the statue and enjoy the lovely view.

A young French sculptor named Frédéric Auguste Bartholdi visited America in 1871. When he saw Bedloe's Island in New York Harbor, he knew it was just the right place for a statue he wanted to build.

Bartholdi had created many other statues and monuments, but this one was to be very special. It was to be a present from the people of France to the people of America, as a remembrance of the old friendship between the two countries.

When Bartholdi got back to Paris, he made sketches and some small models. The statue would be a woman whom he would call Liberty. She would be a symbol of the freedom in the New World. She would hold a lamp in her raised hand to welcome people who came to America. She would be *Liberty Enlightening the World.*

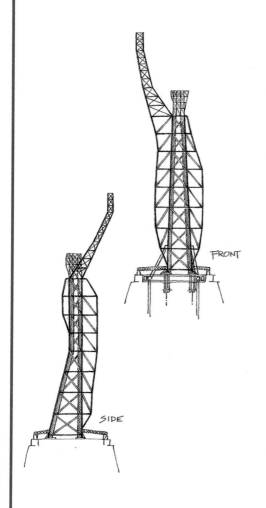

The statue would be very large and very strong. Bartholdi wanted people to be able to climb up inside the statue and look out over the harbor from the crown and torch.

Many well-known artists, engineers, and craftsmen gave him ideas about how to build the statue. First, a huge skeleton was constructed from strong steel.

Many people worked together in a large workshop. Some worked on Liberty's head and crown. Others worked on her right hand which would hold the torch.

In her left hand she would hold a tablet with the date July 4, 1776, written on it. This is when the Declaration of Independence was signed.

The arm holding the torch was sent to
Philadelphia for America's 100th birthday
celebration in 1876. Afterward, it stood in
Madison Square in New York City for a number
of years.

Liberty's head was shown at the World's Fair in Paris during this time. Visitors were able to climb inside and look around. In this way, money was raised to pay for the statue.

Then, skin of gleaming copper was put onto the skeleton and held in place with iron straps. As the huge statue grew, all of Paris watched with great fascination.

Finally, in 1884, Liberty was completed. There was a big celebration in Paris. Many famous people came to see her. Only a few had the energy to climb all the way to the crown— 168 steps!

Then began the hard work of taking Liberty apart for the long voyage across the Atlantic Ocean. Each piece was marked and packed into a crate. There were 214 crates in all. They were carried by train and then put on a ship to America.

But in America people had lost interest in the Statue of Liberty. Money had run out and work on Bedloe's Island had stopped. The base for the statue was not finished. With the help of a large New York newspaper, the money was raised.

People all over the country, including children, sent in whatever they could. By the time the ship reached New York in 1885, it was greeted with new excitement.

The work on the island went on and soon the pedestal was completed. Piece by piece, the skeleton was raised. Then the copper skin was riveted in place. Liberty was put back together like a giant puzzle. The statue had been built not once, but twice!

At last, in 1886, Liberty was standing where she belonged. A wonderful celebration was held. Boats and ships filled the harbor. Speeches were read, songs were sung. Bartholdi himself unveiled Liberty's face and she stood gleaming in all her glory, for everyone to see. There was a great cheer from the crowd. Then President Grover Cleveland gave a speech.

Over the years, immigrants have arrived to begin new lives in America. To them, the Statue of Liberty is a symbol of all their hopes and dreams. She has welcomed millions of people arriving in New York by ship.

Every year, on the Fourth of July, the United States of America celebrates its independence. Fireworks light up the sky above New York Harbor. The Statue of Liberty is a truly unforgettable sight—a symbol of all that is America.

The Story of the Statue of Liberty

Meet the Author

Betsy Maestro was a teacher before she began working with her husband on children's books. She enjoys writing nonfiction books, like "The Story of the Statue of Liberty," for children. She spent months taking notes about the Statue of Liberty in order to write this story. She said, *"Children often become frustrated when a project can't be finished instantly. Our book, we hope, will help them appreciate that it took Bartholdi fifteen years to complete the Statue of Liberty."*

Meet the Illustrator

Giulio Maestro wrote to Walt Kelly, an artist he admired. Mr. Kelly wrote him back, encouraging him to draw every day. *"I think back a lot to the advice Walt Kelly gave me. 'Draw every day. Draw anything and everything you like. The important thing is to draw every day.' It's the same advice I now give children who ask me how they can learn to draw well."*

Mr. Maestro uses a variety of styles and mediums. By using different styles, he can make his work interesting and better describe the mood of the story.

Theme Connections

Think About It

Here are some questions to think about:

- Who built the Statue of Liberty and why?
- What were some of the problems in getting the statue built and brought to America?
- Why is the Statue of Liberty such an important landmark?

Check the Concept/Question Board and answer any questions you can. Post any new questions you have. The next story may answer the questions.

Record Ideas

 Record in your Writing Journal the ideas that you thought about and talked about with others.

Make a Chart

Make a chart to record the steps in the building of the Statue of Liberty.

- In the left-hand column, list the important years that are given in the selection.
- In the right-hand column, explain what important event or events happened each year.
- For example, your chart might look like this:

Year	Important Event
1871	—Bartholdi decides where to build statue —models and sketches were made

Statue of Liberty

Myra Cohn Livingston

Give me your tired, your poor, she says,
Those yearning to be free.
Take a light from my burning torch,
The light of Liberty.

Give me your huddled masses
Lost on another shore,
Tempest-tossed and weary,
These I will take and more.

Give me your thirsty, your hungry
Who come from another place.
You who would dream of freedom
Look into my face.

New Hope

by Henri Sorensen

Jimmy loved to visit Grandpa. He loved the old-fashioned ice-cream store in New Hope, where Grandpa lived. He loved the recycling dump. And he especially loved the statue in the park. "Who is that man?" Jimmy always asked. And every time, Grandpa told him the same wonderful story.

"That's Lars Jensen," Grandpa began.
"Over one hundred years ago, in 1885,
Lars sailed to this country from Denmark.
He brought his wife, Karen, and their two
children, Peter and Mathilde, to start a new
life in America.

"When they landed in New York, they took a train to Minnesota. There Lars bought a wagon, two horses, a hunting rifle, tools, a tent, several bags of seeds, and plenty of food for the trip. Then he and Karen and Peter and Mathilde began the last part of their long journey. On narrow trails, they traveled through forests and forded rivers and crossed the wide plains.

"Sometimes they joined up with other travelers and Peter and Mathilde fell asleep to tales of Sitting Bull told around the campfire. One night a yellow dog appeared at the campsite. 'He must have followed us from the town we passed through this morning,' said Karen. 'Well, we can't take him back now,' said Lars. So Peter and Mathilde adopted him. They named him Fido.

"One day, just as they came to a river, one of the axles on their wagon broke. Lars took off his hat and scratched his head. Fish were jumping in the river. A doe and her fawn stood at the edge of the forest. *'Pokkers!'* said Lars. 'This looks like a good place. Let's stop here.'

"By the time the first snow fell, they had planted and harvested their first crop and built a small cabin for themselves and a shed for their horses. Each morning after checking their traps, Lars and Peter worked on the fence until Karen called them in for hot stew and bread.

"The following spring, while Karen and Mathilde worked in the garden, Lars and Peter built a small ferry. All that summer Lars ferried people and wagons across the river. Business was brisk—Lars's ferry was the only way to cross the river for miles.

"One day a blacksmith named Franz arrived. A busy ferry landing would bring lots of business, so instead of crossing the river, he stayed to build a forge.

"Soon lumbermen arrived to harvest the rich forests and farmers began to clear the land for their crops. 'All these people need a general store,' said Lars, so he traveled several days to the nearest big town to buy rope and shoes and nails and fabric and all the other things he knew the people would need. He named his shop the New Hope General Store.

"As the years passed, more and more people came to the village by the river. The old slow-moving ferry was replaced by a wooden bridge. Now that crossing the river was so easy, the stage coach began to stop at the New Hope General Store. One day a traveler named Saul got off the stage and stayed. Three months later he opened the New Hope Hotel.

"New Hope became a busy, bustling place. A wagon builder set up shop next door to the general store. Then came a bank and a stable and a barbershop and a newspaper office. The *New Hope Gazette* printed all the news and invitations and signs too. Soon Main Street had shops on both sides and a church with a bell in its steeple at the north end.

   "In 1900, Mathilde married Franz's son
Heinrich in that very church, and the whole
town came to celebrate the wedding.
Mathilde and Heinrich moved into a house
on the brand-new street of Maple Lane, and
Heinrich built the New Hope Tannery to
make the best leather gloves and saddles
and boots west of the Appalachian Mountains.

"By 1910, when Mathilde's little boy, Hans, was four years old, the railroad had come to New Hope. On it came traveling actors and salesmen and businessmen and friends and some people who stayed and became new citizens."

"And then what, Grandpa?" Jimmy asked.

"And then came me," said Grandpa. "Hans grew up to be my daddy and your great-grandpa."

"Tell about the statue," said Jimmy.

"When I was five years old," said Grandpa, "New Hope built this statue, and your great-grandpa told me the story that I just told you. It's a statue of Lars Jensen—your great-great-great-grandfather—who started this town because his axle broke."

New Hope

by Henri Sorensen

Meet the Author and Illustrator

Henri Sorensen was born in Denmark. As a young boy, he often visited the local art museum once or twice a week. Later he went on to study art at a university in Denmark. He became a freelance illustrator, working mostly for publishing and advertising companies.

The mood of a story is very important to him. He sees the mood of the pictures in his head before he starts to illustrate. He said, *"When I illustrate a book, I always hope that my illustrations will appeal both to grown-ups and to children. I'm often surprised to see how much children notice and how important colors are to them."* "New Hope" is the first book he has both written and illustrated.

Theme Connections

Think About It

Here are some things to think about:

- Why didn't Lars Jensen know where he would settle when he came to America?
- Why is New Hope a good name for the town started by Lars Jensen?
- What does the selection teach us about how new towns, cities, and villages get started?

Post any new questions you have about Our Country and Its People on the Concept/Question Board and answer any questions you can.

Record Ideas

Record the ideas that you thought about in your Writing Journal. You may list your ideas or present them in a chart form.

Make a Web

- Write "New Hope" in the middle of a page of your Writing Journal.
- Make a web by writing the characters' names and skills each one brought to the town, and drawing lines to connect them to "New Hope."
- Imagine what skills people later brought to the town. Add those to the web also.

FINE Art

The Oregon Trail. 1869. **Albert Bierstadt.** Oil on canvas.
The Butler Institute of American Art, Youngstown, Ohio.

The Telegram, Detention Room, Ellis Island. 1922. **Martha Walter.** Oil on canvas. 14 × 18 in. The National Museum of Women in the Arts, Washington, D.C. Gift of Wallace and Wilhelmina Holladay.

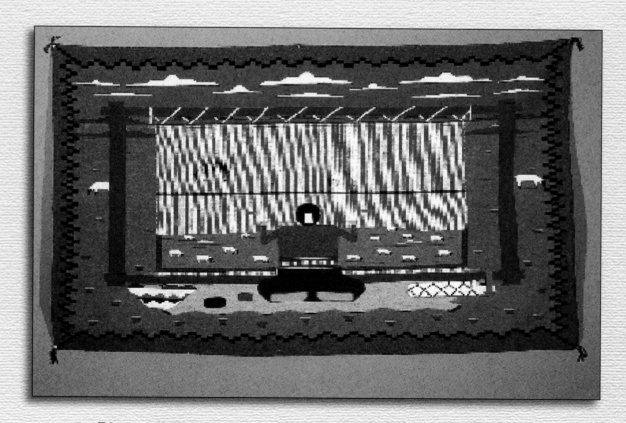

Pictorial Weaving. 1885. **Isabel John.** Wool, commercial, and natural dyes. 48 × 77 $\frac{1}{2}$ in. Collection of The Birmingham Museum of Art, Birmingham, Alabama; Museum purchase in memory of Richard Kenneth McRae, with funds from family and friends.

The Butterfly Seeds

by Mary Watson

Jake's house was empty, except for the overstuffed trunk in the middle of the floor.

"Sit on it, Mama," Papa instructed.

His sisters giggled as they watched Mama bounce up and down while Papa tried to close the latch.

But Jake just stared out the window. He kept thinking about how much he would miss Grandpa.

When Grandpa came to say good-bye, he brought presents for everyone. But he gave Jake something special.

"They're butterfly seeds," Grandpa said, poking around in the little tin box. "Just plant them in your new garden, and, like magic, you'll have hundreds of butterflies."

"Are you sure they will grow in America, Grandpa?" Jake asked sadly. Grandpa pressed the little box tightly into Jake's hand and nodded.

That evening, Jake's family crowded onto the deck of the great S.S. *Celtic*. Many of the passengers were carrying balls of yarn with the ends trailing over the side of the boat.

When the ship pulled away from the dock, those left behind held the ends and watched the lines stretch out across the ocean. Jake could barely see Grandpa when his yarn-line was pulled from his hand. He reached into his pocket to make sure Grandpa's seeds were safe.

That night, the ship tossed, rolling the passengers back and forth in their narrow bunk beds. Jake couldn't sleep. He reached over and slipped his hand into his jacket pocket.

"What do you have there?" Benny asked. The boys moved closer to the dim cabin light.

"They're butterfly seeds," Jake said, opening the tin.

"What kind of seeds?" a few sleepy-eyed children asked as they crawled down from their bunk.

Then Jake told them about Grandpa's seeds, and the beautiful butterfly garden he would plant in America.

"Look what I'm bringing to America!" Benny exclaimed.

And then the show-and-tell game began. Benny let everyone hold his real gold pocket watch. Jake's sisters paraded their porcelain dolls. There were spinning tops, hand-painted eggs, musical instruments, and even a lucky horseshoe. But everyone agreed that Jake's butterfly seeds were the best of all. Except Albert.

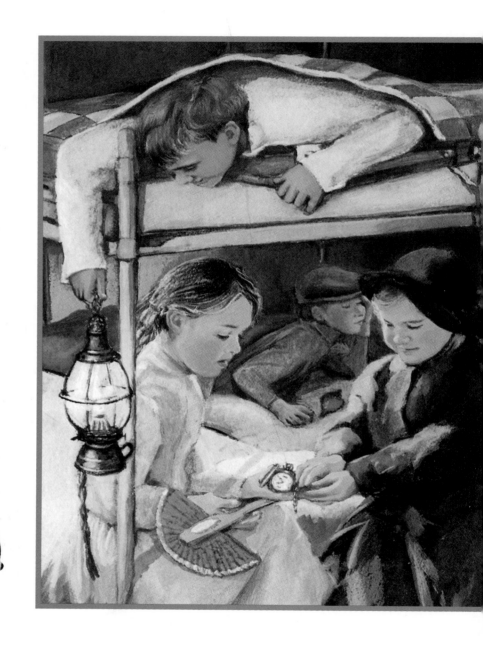

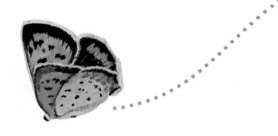

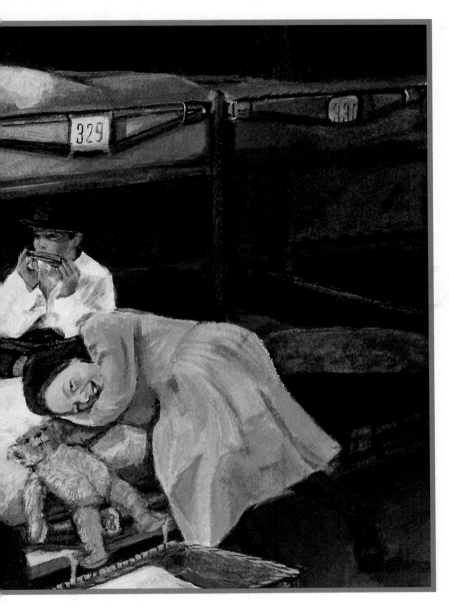

"Whoever heard of butterfly seeds?" he said, and just played his harmonica.

After two long weeks, the ship docked in New York. Papa held tightly to Mama and the children as everyone was herded onto the waiting ferryboats.

When the ferries reached Ellis Island, the passengers were shuffled into long lines to be inspected. Jake's heart raced, as he slowly inched up in line. He wondered if they would take away his seeds. The inspectors looked in Jake's ears and eyes—but not in his pockets. Grandpa's seeds were safe!

Finally, Jake and his family arrived at their new home on Market Street. Papa led the family up three flights of stairs to two small rooms.

Jake looked out at the dark narrow alley, cluttered with lines of drying clothes. *Where can I plant Grandpa's seeds?* he worried.

The next morning, Jake was up early. Below, he spotted a fruit vendor emptying a crate of apples into his cart.

"Could I have that empty crate, sir?" he yelled down.

Before Mr. Gargiulo could figure out where the question had come from, Jake was standing breathlessly beside him.

"I'm going to make a window box . . . so I can plant my grandpa's seeds in it . . . and that's why I need the crate," he blurted out.

"You can have the crate, boy, but I don't think it's any good for planting seeds." Mr. Gargiulo wiggled his fingers between the slats.

"All you need is a piece of burlap to fix that," called Mr. Lingchow, the fish peddler.

He emptied his catch into an icy bin and handed Jake the empty bag. Jake opened the seam with his pocketknife and spread the burlap evenly inside the crate.

Jake hurried across the street to the blacksmith shop to show Papa. It was Papa's first day at his new job, and he didn't pay much attention when Jake asked for his advice.

"I need a way to keep this crate from falling off our windowsill," Jake shouted over the ring of the anvil.

"Maybe I can help you," someone hollered. It was Mr. O'Malley, the shop owner. He knew just what Jake needed. He hammered two bars of red-hot metal into a strong pair of window-box hangers.

After work, Papa nailed the box into place. Jake rigged up a clothesline and a pulley to hoist up buckets of dirt from the alley. All of the neighborhood children wanted to help. All except for Albert, who played his harmonica instead.

It was a hot summer. Jake and his new friends climbed the fire escape every day to check the window box. They would hang over the railing and search through the bushy plants for butterflies.

"Maybe your silly old grandpa got the seeds mixed up," Albert would mutter.

Jake began to wonder if Grandpa's seeds were magic or just a story made up for a homesick boy.

Then one day the sky rumbled, and a sudden shower drenched the hot, steaming streets.

When the sun reappeared, merchants and shoppers filled the street once more. The children went back to their play.

Suddenly, Mr. Gargiulo called out, "Look at that beautiful butterfly."

The children chased the butterfly through the crowded street until it flew up to Jake's window box.

"Look at them all!" Albert shouted.

Jake heard Albert's yell and opened his window.

"They're finally here, Grandpa!" Jake whispered, as if Grandpa were listening. "Your butterflies are here . . . and they like America too."

The Butterfly Seeds

Meet the Author and Illustrator

Mary Watson's husband wrote the first picture book she illustrated. Her grandfather inspired her second book, "The Butterfly Seeds." Her grandparents met on the boat on their trip to the United States. Her grandfather brought seeds from England, and her grandmother brought seeds from Ireland. He told her many stories of the trip.

Ms. Watson finds painting people and faces more interesting than painting a landscape. She and her family live in New Jersey. They operate a historical farm. She often illustrates and writes materials for the farm.

Theme Connections

Think About It

Here are some things to think about:

- Why do you think Jake's grandpa gave him the seeds?
- How did the butterfly seeds help Jake adjust to his new home in America?
- What does the selection teach us about the hopes and dreams of immigrants?

Check the Concept/Question Board and answer any questions you can. Post any new questions you have about Our Country and Its People.

Record Ideas

Record in your Writing Journal the ideas that you thought about and talked about with others.

Make a Wheel of Hope

Draw a wheel in your Writing Journal with space between the spokes to write on them.

- On each spoke write down something that Jake was hoping for in the story. For example, at the beginning of the story Jake is hoping not to leave home.
- Complete your wheel by filling in all the spokes in order with different things Jake hoped for.

A Very Important Day

Maggie Rugg Herold

illustrated by Catherine Stock

Nelia Batungbakal was too excited to
sleep. She was looking out her
window, listening to music on her
Walkman, when she thought she saw snow!

Sure enough, before long the station DJ came
on. "It's three A.M. here in New York City, and
it's snowing. Four to six inches are expected
by noon."

Nelia's mind raced. Imagine, snow on such a very important day. This would never happen in the Philippines. Her son and daughter-in-law and the grandchildren were fast asleep. She would need to awaken them early, to allow extra time for the trip downtown.

"Wake up, Miguel. It's snowing," Rosa Huerta
called to her brother. "There are at least two
inches on the fire escape."

"All *right!*" said Miguel, bounding from his
room. He opened the window and scooped up
some snow.

"Close that window," their father ordered.
"It's cold in here, and—Miguel, is that snow in your hand?"

"Yes, Papa, the first this year."

"Back outside with it before it melts. And on such a very important day. This would not happen in Mexico, at least not in the south."

"Let's move quickly," urged their mother. "It's six-thirty. We can get an early start downtown."

Veena Patel had just set the table when the doorbell rang. "That will be the children," her husband, Mohandas, said.

But it was their neighbors, the Pitambers. They apologized for stopping by so early. "We were afraid of missing you, and we wanted to wish you well on this very important day."

"Join us for breakfast," said Veena. "Our daughter and her family will be here any minute. They think we must allow extra time, that the snow will slow us down. That's one worry we never had in India."

The doorbell rang again, and this time it was the children. Everyone gathered quickly at the table, talking eagerly about the special morning ahead.

Out the door and down the steps came the
Leonovs—first Eugenia, then her brother, Lev,
followed by their grandfather, grandmother,
mother, and father.

"Snow reminds me of Russia," said their mother.

"I love snow!" exclaimed Eugenia.

Her grandfather stooped, grabbed two handfuls, and threw them at his grandchildren.

The fight was on.

Just then Mr. Dionetti lobbed a snowball from
the door of his corner grocery. "Is this
the big day?" he called out. "Are you headed
downtown?"

"Yes," answered their father. "This snowball
fight is headed for the subway."

"Congratulations!" cried Mr. Dionetti. And tossing a big handful of snow straight up in the air, he crossed the street to shake their hands.

Kostas and Nikos Soutsos were clearing the sidewalk in front of the family restaurant when their mother came out the side door from their apartment above. She was carrying their baby sister, Kiki.

"Kiki, this is snow," said Kostas.

"How do you like it?" Nikos asked.

Kiki seemed puzzled by the flakes that hit her nose.

Their mother laughed. "She'll get used to it, living here. Not like Greece, where it snows maybe once in ten years. But where's your father? We should be on our way."

"He went to make a sign for the door. See, there he is."

"Set those shovels inside, and let's be off," their father called. "And read this sign, everyone. What does it say?"

They chorused together, "Closed for a very important day."

"Finally! There's the bus," said Duong Hao.

He and his older sister, Trinh, brushed snow off each other and followed their mother on board. It was crowded at first, but a few stops later they all got seats.

"Here we are," said their mother, "in the middle of a snowstorm on the most important day since we arrived from Vietnam—"

Suddenly the driver braked hard.

They were all thrown forward.

"Car skidded at the light and couldn't stop," the driver yelled. "Everybody okay?"

Fortunately only bundles had landed on the floor.

"That was close," said their mother.

"Yes," said Trinh, "but our driver's good."

Duong nodded. "Maybe he knows that today of all days we just have to get downtown."

"I love the ferry," said Jorge Báez.

"So do I," agreed his cousin Pedro Jiménez, "especially in snow. Let's go up on deck."

"Not by yourselves, but I'll go with you," said Pedro's father.

"And I'll keep you company," Jorge's father added.

"Me too," begged Jorge's sister. "I want to go outside."

"All right," said her father. "You are old enough."

They went up on deck, leaving the little ones inside with Jorge's mother and aunt.

"I'm so glad this day takes us across the harbor," said Pedro's father. "I never tire of the ride."

"Neither do I," said Jorge's father. "Even in snow, this view is the best in the city. And now we will all remember it as part of the most important day since we came from the Dominican Republic."

Through the narrow streets on the unshoveled sidewalks the Zeng family made their way on foot. Suddenly, from above them, a voice called out.

Yujin's friend Bailong was leaning out the window. "I've been watching for you," he said. "Don't open this until later. Catch!"

Down through the snowflakes came a small brightly wrapped package, straight into Yujin's outstretched hands.

"Thanks, Bailong."

"Thanks for remembering."

"This is such an important day."

"The most important since we arrived from China."

Yujin tucked the package safely inside his coat, and with waves and good-byes the Zengs set off again, heading south.

Jihan Idris and her parents had also left home early to make the trip downtown. Now their subway ride was over, and there was time for breakfast.

"I see a coffee shop ahead," Jihan's mother called out.

"I want to sit at the counter!" Jihan exclaimed.

They entered and sat on three stools, Jihan in the middle.

"I'd like waffles," Jihan told their waitress.

"And I'll have pancakes," said her father. "With coffee and grapefruit juice."

"Scrambled eggs and a toasted bagel, please," said her mother. "With orange juice and tea."

Quickly the waitress was back with their breakfasts. "What brings you out so early on a snowy day like today?" she asked.

"Can you guess?" said Jihan's mother.

"It's the most important day for us since we came from Egypt," said Jihan's father.

"And I'm celebrating with waffles," said Jihan. "I never get them at home."

"There's the courthouse," said Kwame Akuffo to his wife, Efua, as they rounded a corner, walking fast.

She stopped. "Only two blocks to go. I'll race you to the steps."

He stopped, too. "Are you crazy?"

"It's not slippery."

"You're on! Ready?"

She nodded.

"On your mark, get set, go!"

And off they dashed, down the sidewalk.

"Tie," Efua declared at the bottom of the steps.

"I used to run in Ghana," Kwame said, "but never in snow."

"Wait," said Efua, taking a camera from her purse.

"Before we go in on this very important day, let's get someone to take our picture."

So they asked a stranger, who gladly obliged, and then hand in hand they climbed the courthouse steps.

As Robert MacTaggart came through the courthouse door, he heard familiar voices calling, "Robert. Over here."

Near the entrance stood his friends Elizabeth and Alan. Each of them gave him a big hug.

"You made it," Robert said. "Thank you so much for coming. I was afraid the snow would stop you."

"Oh, no, not on such an important day," said Elizabeth.

"We were getting worried about *you*, though," said Alan.

Robert chuckled. "A few snowflakes defeat a man from the highlands of Scotland? Come on. Let's find the chamber. It's on this floor."

Leaving relatives and friends to wait in the hall outside, Alvaro Castro, his wife, Romelia, and their children entered the crowded chamber. They were among the last to find seats.

Soon the examiner appeared, and the room became quiet. "When I call your name," he said, "please come forward to receive your certificate."

Many names were called; many people went forward. Then, "Alvaro and Romelia Castro and children Marta, José, and Oscar."

The Castros approached the examiner.

"Please sign here," he said to Alvaro. "And here," he said to Romelia. "These are your papers."

"Thank you," said Alvaro. "This is a proud moment."

The Castros returned to their seats. "The long journey from El Salvador has ended," Romelia whispered to her husband, and he squeezed her hand.

When the examiner had finished, he said, "Please open the door to relatives and friends."

People poured in. There were so many they filled the aisles and lined the walls at the back and sides of the chamber.

"Everyone please rise," said the examiner, and as everyone did, a judge entered the chamber.

"Your Honor," said the examiner, "these petitioners have qualified for citizenship in the United States of America."

"Then," said the judge, "will you repeat after me the oath of citizenship. Let us begin, 'I hereby declare, on oath . . .'"

"I hereby declare, on oath . . ."

Echoing the judge phrase by phrase, sentence by sentence, the many voices resounded as one, swearing loyalty to the United States of America.

"Congratulations," said the judge. "Those of you who can be, please be seated."

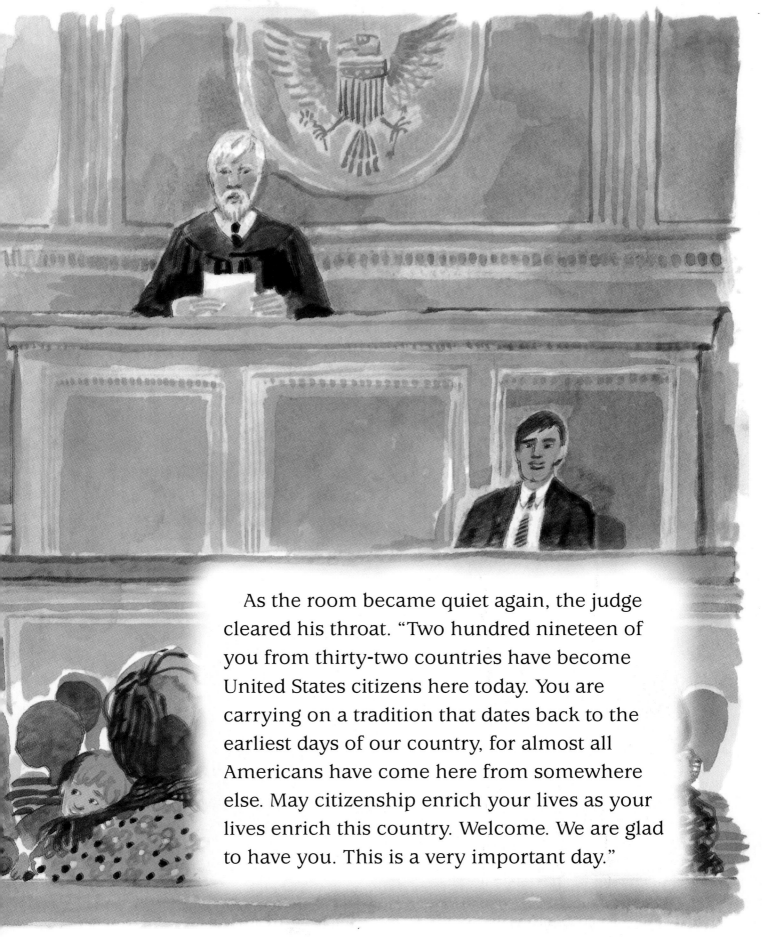

As the room became quiet again, the judge cleared his throat. "Two hundred nineteen of you from thirty-two countries have become United States citizens here today. You are carrying on a tradition that dates back to the earliest days of our country, for almost all Americans have come here from somewhere else. May citizenship enrich your lives as your lives enrich this country. Welcome. We are glad to have you. This is a very important day."

Everyone then rose and joined the judge in the Pledge of Allegiance.

Family and friends and strangers turned to one another. "Best wishes!" "I'm so happy for you." "You must be so proud." "Isn't it wonderful?" "What a day!" "Let me shake your hand." "Let me give you a kiss." "Let me give you a hug."

Zeng Yujin tore open the package from his friend Bailong. Inside he found small American flags, a dozen or so, enough to share with everyone in his family and with other new citizens surrounding him.

In a wave of excitement, they all made their way out of the chamber, through the hallway, and back to the courthouse door.

"Look!" they exclaimed, everybody talking at once. "The snow has stopped." "The sun is shining." "It will be easy to get home and go on celebrating." "This has become our country on this very important day!"

A Very Important Day

Meet the Author

Maggie Rugg Herold's first book for children is *"A Very Important Day."* The idea for the book came when Catherine Stock, the illustrator, became a U.S. citizen. Catherine Stock asked her to write a children's book about this special day. Maggie Herold thought it would be more interesting to write about many families, rather than just one.

When she was asked what you need to be a good writer, she said, *"Being a good observer, that's where it all starts."*

Meet the Illustrator

Catherine Stock was born in Sweden. When she was growing up, she loved books and was always painting. Her mother was a painter. Stock's family moved a lot. She has lived in France, England, South Africa, the United States, and Hong Kong. All of these places have given her many memories to use in her paintings. She has also written books for children.

352

Theme Connections

Think About It

Here are some things to think about:
- Why was the day so very important to all the people in the story?
- What is important about the snowstorm?
- What does the selection teach us about the people of America?

Check the Concept/Question Board and answer any questions you can. Post any new questions you have.

Record Ideas

 Record in your Writing Journal the ideas that you thought about and talked about with others. Your ideas may be a list or in a chart form.

Make a Chart

- Make a chart with two columns.
- In the left-hand column, write the names of the different countries given in the story.
- Use the right-hand column to write one way each country is different from the United States. Your chart may look like this:

Country	Different from USA
Egypt	don't eat waffles

Jalapeño Bagels

Natasha Wing
illustrated by Robert Casilla

"What should I bring to school on Monday for International Day?" I ask my mother. "My teacher told us to bring something from our culture."

"You can bring a treat from the *panaderia*," she suggests. Panaderia is what Mama calls our bakery. "Help us bake on Sunday—then you can pick out whatever you want."

354

"It's a deal," I tell her. I like helping at the bakery. It's warm there, and everything smells so good.

Early Sunday morning, when it is still dark, my mother wakes me up.

"Pablo, it's time to go to work," she says.

We walk down the street to the bakery. My father turns on the lights. My mother turns on the ovens. She gets out the pans and ingredients for *pan dulce*. Pan dulce is Mexican sweet bread.

I help my mother mix and knead the dough. She shapes rolls and loaves of bread and slides them into the oven. People tell her she makes the best pan dulce in town.

"Maybe I'll bring pan dulce to school," I tell her.

Next we make *empanadas de calabaza*—
pumpkin turnovers. I'm in charge of
spooning the pumpkin filling. Mama folds
the dough in half and presses the edges with
a fork. She bakes them until they are flaky
and golden brown. Some customers come to
our bakery just for her turnovers.

"Maybe I'll bring empanadas de calabaza
instead."

"You'll figure it out," she says. "Ready to make *chango* bars?" Chango means "monkey man."

Mama lets me pour in the chocolate chips and nuts. When she's not looking, I pour in more chocolate chips.

"I could bring chango bars. They're my favorite dessert."

"Mine, too," says Mama. "This batch should be especially good. I put in extra chips."

My father calls from the back room.
"Pablo! Come help me with the bagels!"
Papa speaks English and Yiddish. He learned
Yiddish from his family in New York City.
I know some words, too. *Bubbe* means
"grandmother." He uses my bubbe's recipe
to make the bagels.

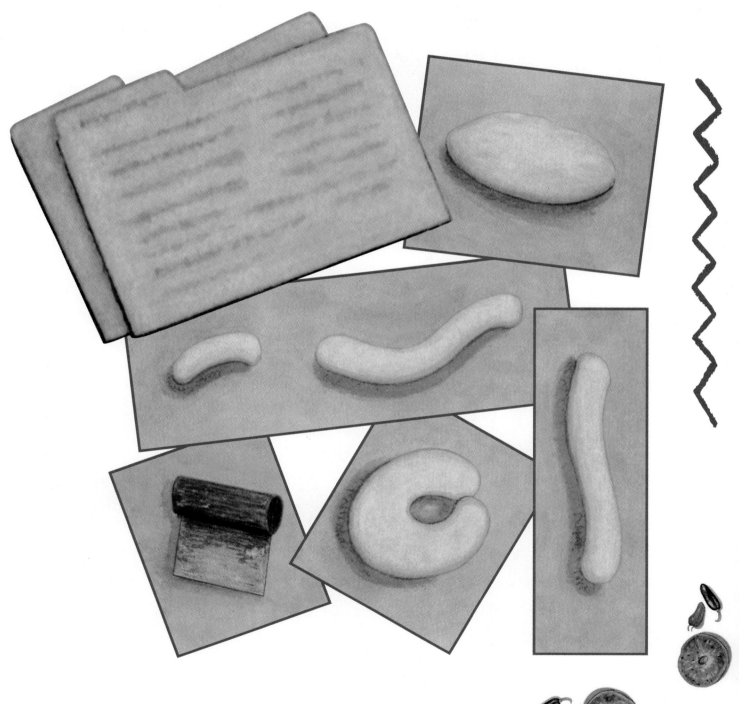

First he makes the dough in a big metal bowl. Then he rolls it out into a long rope shape. He cuts off pieces and shows me how to connect the ends in a circle. We put the circles on trays where they sit and rise.

While we are waiting my father makes *challah*, Jewish braided bread. He lets me practice braiding challah dough at my own counter. It's a lot like braiding hair. The customers say it is almost too beautiful to eat.

"Maybe I'll bring a loaf of challah to school," I tell Papa. He smiles.

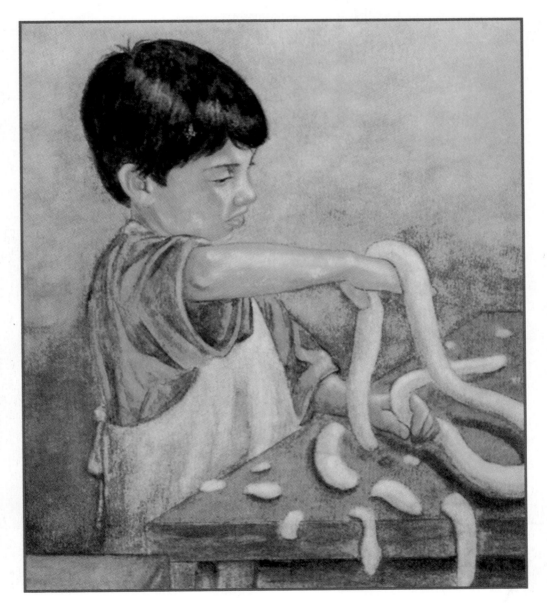

When the bagel dough has risen, he boils the bagels in a huge pot of water and fishes them out with a long slotted spoon. I sprinkle on poppy seeds and sesame seeds, and then they go in the oven.

"Maybe I could bring sesame-seed bagels with cream cheese."

362

"No *lox?*" Lox is smoked salmon. My father's favorite bagel is pumpernickel with a smear of cream cheese and lox.

I crinkle my nose. "Lox tastes like fish. Jam is better."

My mother joins us and helps my father make another batch of bagels—*jalapeño* bagels. My parents use their own special recipe. While Papa kneads the dough, Mama chops the jalapeño *chiles*. She tosses them into the dough and adds dried red peppers. We roll, cut, make circles, and let them rise. I can't wait until they are done because I am getting hungry.

"Have you decided what you're going to bring to school?" asks Mama.

"It's hard to choose. Everything is so good," I tell her. I look at Papa. "Except for lox."

"You should decide before we open," warns Mama, "or else our customers will buy everything up."

I walk past all the sweet breads, chango bars, and bagels.

I think about my mother and my father and all the different things they make in the bakery.

And suddenly I know exactly what I'm going to bring.

"Jalapeño bagels," I tell my parents. "And I'll spread them with cream cheese and jam."

"Why jalapeño bagels?" asks Papa.

"Because they are a mixture of both of you. Just like me!"

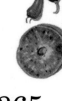

Jalapeño Bagels

Meet the Author

Natasha Wing was born in Milford, Connecticut. Her first job was working at a newspaper. She later worked for an advertising agency. She is now the owner of a writing company.

She became interested in writing children's books after reading one as an adult. She said, *"When you put two things together, such as a story and illustrations, the result is greater than what you expected."* "Jalapeño Bagels" is her second book for children.

Meet the Illustrator

Robert Casilla was born in Jersey City, New Jersey. He began illustrating after graduating from the School of Visual Arts. He said, *"I find great rewards and satisfaction in illustrating for children."* He enjoys working with watercolors for his illustrations. Many of his illustrations are for biographies. When he illustrates a biography, he tries to learn a lot about the person. Knowing the person very well helps him when he works on the art.

Theme Connections

Think About It

Here are some questions to think about:

- Why is it so difficult for the boy in the story to choose a favorite food to bring to school?
- Why did he decide to bring jalapeño bagels?
- What does the selection teach us about appreciating differences in people?

Check the Concept/Question Board and answer any questions you can.

Record Ideas

Record in your Writing Journal the ideas that you thought about and talked about with others. You may choose to simply list your ideas or to present them in a chart form.

Make a List

- Make a list of foods you have eaten that you think are from other countries.
- Beside each food put the country you think it comes from. For example, "spaghetti" is considered Italian food so write "Italy" beside it.
- Work with a partner to come up with as many different foods and countries as you can.

Bibliography

The American Wei

by Marion Hess Pomeranc. Will the tooth fairy find Wei Fong now that he's an American citizen? Read and find out.

Father's Rubber Shoes

by Yumi Heo. How does his father's story about a pair of rubber shoes help a young Korean immigrant make new friends?

Frida Maria: A Story of the Old Southwest

by Deborah Nourse Lattimore. What happens to Frida Maria's frilly dress when she enters a horse race at the fiesta?

Grandmother and the Runaway Shadow

by Liz Rosenberg. Have you made friends with your shadow lately? Meet a young Russian girl who did just that.

Grandfather's Journey

by Allen Say. You can't be two places at the same time, but if you could, would you want to be? Some people do.

Mama Provi and the Pot of Rice

by Sylvia Rosa-Casanova. A pot of rice becomes a feast as it makes a trip up seven flights of stairs. What's happening here?

Red Bird

by Barbara Mitchell. Why does Jenny become Red Bird once a year?

What Zeesie Saw on Delancey Street

by Elsa Okon Rael. What happens when you go somewhere you're not supposed to go and see something you're not meant to see? Zeesie finds out.

Writer's Handbook

Table *of* Contents

Grammar, Mechanics, and Usage

Writer's Handbook

Grammar, Mechanics, and Usage

Kinds of Sentences

Rule: A **sentence** is a group of words that tells a complete thought. It begins with a capital letter and ends with a punctuation mark.

A sentence can tell about something, ask about something, or show strong feeling about something. Each of these three different kinds of sentences ends with a different punctuation mark.

A sentence that tells about something is called a statement. It ends with a period.

Statement: The dog ran home.

A sentence that asks something is called a question. It ends with a question mark.

Question: Did you see the dog?

A sentence that shows strong feeling about something is called an exclamation. It ends with an exclamation point.

Exclamation: That dog is really fast!

Writer's Handbook

Grammar, Mechanics, and Usage

Combining Sentences

Rule: Two sentences with ideas that are alike can be put together, or combined, by using the word *and*.

You can use the word *and* to combine two sentences if they are about ideas that are alike. Place a comma before the word *and*.

Two Sentences: Rosa walked to the mailbox. She mailed the letter.

Combined Sentence: Rosa walked to the mailbox, <u>and</u> she mailed the letter.

Do not use *and* to combine two sentences that are not about things that are alike. Do not combine these kinds of sentences.

Two Sentences: The letter was for Rosa's friend. Rosa walked home.

Writer's Handbook

Grammar, Mechanics, and Usage

Parts of a Sentence

Rule: A sentence is made up of two parts: a **subject** and a **predicate.** Without these two parts, a group of words is not a complete sentence.

Every sentence has a **subject.** The subject names the person or thing the sentence is about. The subject is underlined in each of these sentences.

> **Subjects:** <u>Jim and Rob</u> are brothers.
>
> <u>Soccer</u> is their favorite sport.
>
> <u>They</u> practice in their backyard.

Every sentence has a **predicate.** The predicate tells what the subject is or does. The predicate is underlined in each of these sentences.

> **Predicates:** Jim and Rob <u>are brothers.</u>
>
> Soccer <u>is their favorite sport.</u>
>
> They <u>practice in their backyard.</u>

Writer's Handbook

Grammar, Mechanics, and Usage

Ending a Sentence with the Right Mark

Rule: End every sentence with a punctuation mark: a period, a question mark, or an exclamation point. Use different end marks for different kinds of sentences.

If a sentence tells about something, it is a statement. End a statement with a **period (.)**.

> **Statement:** José has a new puppy.

If a sentence asks something, it is a question. End a question with a **question mark (?)**.

> **Question:** Can you hear the puppy bark?

If a sentence shows strong feeling, it is an exclamation. End an exclamation with an **exclamation mark (!)**.

> **Exclamation:** It's such a loud puppy!

Grammar, Mechanics, and Usage

Using Commas with Lists in a Sentence

Rule: In a list of three or more things of the same type, put a comma after each word that comes before *and* or *or*.

In a list of three or more persons, places, or things, use a comma after each word that comes before *and* or *or*.

Things: Frogs eat <u>bugs</u>, <u>worms</u>, and <u>spiders</u>.

In a list of three or more descriptive words, use a comma after each word that comes before *and* or *or*.

Descriptive Words: The bullfrog is <u>large</u>, <u>green</u>, and <u>powerful</u>.

In a list of three or more action words, use a comma after each word that comes before *and* or *or*.

Action Words: The frogs <u>croak</u>, <u>leap</u>, or <u>hop</u> about.

Grammar, Mechanics, and Usage

Using Commas in Dates, Addresses, and Letters

Rule: Use commas in dates, in addresses when names of places are used, and in letters.

In dates, use a comma between the day and the year.

Dates: My Aunt Maria was born March 17, 1973.

Her baby was born June 29, 1992.

In addresses, use a comma between the parts of a place name.

Addresses: Aunt Maria now lives in Dallas, Texas.

Her baby was born in Richmond, Virginia.

In a friendly letter, use a comma after the greeting, or words you use to say hello, and in the closing, the words you use to say good-bye.

Greeting: Dear Aunt Maria,

Closing: Love,

Using Parentheses

Rule: Parentheses are punctuation marks. Use parentheses to show information that is added to the sentence.

Put parentheses around extra information in a sentence. The information may tell what one of the words in the sentence means. It may also tell the reader more about another part of the sentence.

> **Extra information about the meaning of one of the words:**
> Ralphie is a canine (dog).

> **Extra information about the idea in the sentence:**
> Columbus's first voyage to North America (1492) was an important event.

Grammar, Mechanics, and Usage

Using Capital Letters

Rule: Always capitalize the first word in a sentence. Always capitalize the word *I*. Capitalize other words only if they are used in a special way.

Begin the first word of a sentence with a capital letter.

First Word: <u>Today</u> the circus comes to town.
<u>My</u> family will go to the circus.

Write the word *I* with a capital letter.

The Word *I*: Will <u>I</u> see lions and tigers?
My sister and <u>I</u> also like the clowns.

Begin names of people and places with capital letters.

People and Places: Dr. Jane R. Smith
Uncle Al   Fifth Avenue   Indian Ocean

Begin the days of the week and months of the year with capital letters.

Days of the Week: Friday   Tuesday
Months of the Year: August 10
the week of May 19

Grammar, Mechanics, and Usage
Using Capital Letters (continued)

Do <u>not</u> begin the seasons of the year with capital letters unless they are the first words of sentences.

winter   spring   summer   autumn   fall

Capitalize words used to show directions only when they are part of the name of a place or the name of a street.

Directions Capitalized:
West Park Street   North Dakota

Directions Not Capitalized:
one block west   north of here

Writer's Handbook

Grammar, Mechanics, and Usage

Kinds of Words (Parts of Speech) and How They Are Used

Rule: Language is made up of different kinds of words. They include **nouns, pronouns, verbs, adjectives,** and **adverbs.**

A **noun** names a person, place, or thing.

> **Nouns:** <u>Alice</u> sings happy <u>songs</u>.

A **pronoun** takes the place of a noun.

> **Pronoun:** Alice sings happy songs.
> <u>She</u> is a singer.

A **verb** names an action or tells what someone or something is, was, or will be.

> **Verbs:** Alice <u>sings</u> happy songs.
> She <u>is</u> a singer.

An **adjective** describes a noun or a pronoun.

> **Adjectives:** Alice is a <u>good</u> singer.
> She is <u>talented</u>.

An **adverb** can describe a verb. It may answer the questions *How? How often? When?* or *Where?*

> **Adverbs:** Alice sings <u>happily</u>.
> She sang two songs <u>today</u>.

Writer's Handbook

Grammar, Mechanics, and Usage

Using Nouns That Show Who Owns Something

Rule: A **possessive noun** is a word that names a person, place, or thing that owns or has something. Possessive nouns are singular or plural.

A singular noun names one person, place, or thing. To make a singular noun possessive, add an apostrophe and an *s ('s)*.

> **Singular Noun:** <u>Maria</u> has two birds.
>
> **Possessive Noun:** <u>Maria's</u> birds are green.

A plural noun names more than one person, place, or thing. Most plural nouns end with *s*. To make a plural noun ending in *s* possessive, just add an apostrophe after the *s (s')*.

> **Plural Noun Ending with** *s:* The <u>girls</u> own two bikes.
>
> **Possessive Noun:** The <u>girls'</u> bikes are new.

Grammar, Mechanics, and Usage

Using Nouns That Show Who Owns Something (continued)

If a plural noun does not end with *s*, add an apostrophe and *s ('s)* just as for the singular form.

Plural Noun Not Ending with *s*:
The <u>children</u> have books on the table.

Possessive Noun: The <u>children's</u> books are on the table.

Writer's Handbook

Grammar, Mechanics, and Usage

Using the Right Pronoun for the Right Noun

Rule: **Pronouns** are words that take the place of nouns. Use pronouns that agree in number with the nouns that they replace.

Singular pronouns stand for one person or thing. Use singular pronouns to take the place of singular nouns.

Singular Nouns and Pronouns:
Ann got a new baseball.
She threw it far.

Plural pronouns stand for more than one person or thing. Use plural pronouns to take the place of plural nouns.

Plural Nouns and Pronouns:
The children were playing.
They played ball.

Grammar, Mechanics, and Usage
Using the Right Pronoun for the Right Noun (continued)

This chart shows some pronouns you use often:

Singular Pronouns	Plural Pronouns
I, me	we, us
you	you
he, she, him, her, it	they, them

Be sure your readers know exactly to whom or what each pronoun refers. If it is not clear to which noun a pronoun refers, use the nouns again.

Not Clear: Kate showed Mary her new coat. <u>She</u> really liked it. (Does *she* refer to Kate or to Mary?)

Clear: Kate showed Mary her new coat. Mary really liked it.

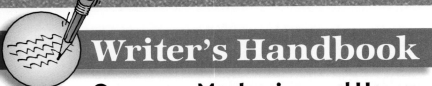

Grammar, Mechanics, and Usage

Using Pronouns That Show Who Owns Something

Rule: A pronoun is a word that takes the place of a noun. It is a word that stands for a person, place, or thing. Use a **possessive pronoun** to show who owns or has something.

Use a possessive pronoun in place of a possessive noun. Here is a list of pronouns that show who owns something:

my, your, his, her, its, our, their

Possessive Noun: The <u>boy's</u> dog ran into the street.
Possessive Pronoun: <u>His</u> dog ran into the street.
(His stands for *boy's.)*

Possessive Noun: The <u>children's</u> pets played outside.
Possessive Pronoun: <u>Their</u> pets played outside.
(Their stands for *children's.)*

Grammar, Mechanics, and Usage
Using Pronouns That Show Who Owns Something (continued)

Do not mix up the pronoun *its* with the word *it's*. *It's* means "it is."

Not a Possessive Pronoun: It's fun to read that book.

Possessive Pronoun: Its pictures are pretty.

Do not mix up the pronoun *your* with the word *you're*. *You're* means "you are."

Not a Possessive Pronoun: You're writing a story.

Possessive Pronoun: Your story is about a circus.

Writer's Handbook

Grammar, Mechanics, and Usage

Telling About What's Happening Now

Rule: Verbs in the **present tense** show action that is happening now. These verbs can also show action that happens again and again.

If the subject of a sentence is singular (only one person, place, or thing), add *-s* to the verb to put it in the present tense. This rule works for most verbs.

Add *-s:* David <u>walks</u> home from school. He <u>climbs</u> the steps to his house. The cat <u>greets</u> David.

Some verbs have special rules for telling what is happening now. If the verb ends with *ch, sh, s, x,* or *z*, add *-es* to a verb that is used with a singular subject.

Add *-es:* David <u>fixes</u> a snack. The cat <u>watches</u> him.

If the verb ends with a consonant followed by *y*, change the *y* to *i* and add *-es*.

Change *y* to *i* and Add *-es:* He <u>hurries</u> across the street.

Grammar, Mechanics, and Usage

Telling About What's Happening Now (continued)

If the subject of a sentence is *I* or *you*, do not add an ending to the verb. Do not add an ending if the subject is plural (more than one).

> **No Ending:** I like a bus. You ride in the car. Boys walk with him. They climb the steps.

Some present-tense verbs have different forms. Pay special attention to them when you write.

Verb	Present-Tense Forms
be	I am. You are. We are. They are. He is. She is. It is.
have	I have. We have. You have. They have. He has. She has. It has.

Writer's Handbook

Grammar, Mechanics, and Usage

Telling About What Happened Before

Rule: Verbs in the **past tense** show action that has already happened.

You can add *-ed* to many verbs to put them in the past tense.

> **Add *-ed*:** Kelly <u>painted</u> a picture. She <u>liked</u> it. She <u>carried</u> it to the kitchen. She <u>showed</u> it to Mom.

You must sometimes follow special rules when you add *-ed* to verbs. If the verb ends with *e*, drop *e* when you add *-ed*.

> **Drop *-e*:** She <u>liked</u> it.

If the verb ends with a consonant followed by *y*, change the *y* to *i* and add *-ed*.

> **Change *y* to *i* and Add *-ed*:** She <u>carried</u> it to the kitchen.

For most verbs that have one syllable, one short vowel, and one final consonant, double that final consonant before adding *-ed*.

> **Double Final Consonant:** Mother <u>stopped</u>. She <u>plugged</u> in the iron.

390

Grammar, Mechanics, and Usage

Telling About What Happened Before (continued)

Some past-tense verbs have special forms. Here are some common examples.

Verb	Past-Tense Forms
be	was, were
do	did
have	had
go	went
come	came
say	said
give	gave

Writer's Handbook

Grammar, Mechanics, and Usage

Using the Right Verb for the Subject

Rule: In a sentence, the verb must **agree** with the subject. A singular subject (only one) takes a singular verb. A plural subject (more than one) takes a plural verb.

The **subject** of a sentence is the word or words that refer to the person or thing that does the action of the verb. The **verb** is the word that refers to the action.

Most verbs follow this pattern in the present tense:

Present Tense	
Singular	*Plural*
I work	we work
you work	you work
he, she, it works	they work

Notice that for all subjects except *he, she,* or *it,* the verb is the same.

Grammar, Mechanics, and Usage
Using the Right Verb for the Subject (continued)

For *he*, *she*, or *it*, and for all subjects that can be referred to as *he*, *she*, or *it*, the verb usually takes the ending -*s*.

> **Subject can be referred to as *he*:**
> Pepe <u>plays</u> soccer.

Verbs that end in -*s*, -*x*, -*ch*, or -*sh* take the ending -*es*.

> **Verb ends in -*ch*:** The goalie <u>touches</u> the ball with his hands.

In verbs that end in a consonant plus *y*, the *y* changes to *i* before the -*es* ending.

> **Verb ends in consonant plus *y*:**
> The baby <u>cries</u> when she is hungry.

Writer's Handbook

Grammar, Mechanics, and Usage

Using Words That Describe (Adjectives and Adverbs)

Rule: An **adjective** is a describing word. Use an adjective to describe a person, place, or thing. An adverb is also a describing word. Use an adverb to tell something about the action in a sentence. An **adverb** can tell when, where, how, or how often the action happened.

An **adjective** describes a person, a place, or a thing.

> **Adjectives:** Marcie found a <u>gold</u> ring.
> The ring was in the <u>old</u> house.

An **adverb** can tell about the action of the sentence. Adverbs tell where, when, how, or how often.

> **Adverbs:** Marcie held the ring <u>carefully</u>. (tells how)
> She took it <u>outside</u>. (tells where)

Many adverbs end in *-ly*.

> **Adverb:** Marcie walked <u>quickly</u>.
> (quick + *-ly*)

Writer's Handbook

Grammar, Mechanics, and Usage

Comparing with Adjectives and Adverbs

Rule: **Adjectives** and **adverbs** are describing words. Adjectives are used to describe people, places, and things. Adverbs are used to describe actions. You can use adjectives and adverbs to compare.

If the adjective has one or two syllables, add the *-er* ending to compare two things. Add the *-est* ending to compare more than two.

> **Examples:** **soft   softer   (the) softest**
>
> **No Comparison:**   This puppy has <u>soft</u> fur.
> **Comparing Two:**   The kitten has <u>softer</u> fur than the puppy.
>
> **Comparing More Than Two:**   The baby hamster has the <u>softest</u> fur of all.

If the adjective has more than two syllables, use the word *more* to compare two things. Use the word *most* to compare more than two. When you use *more* or *most*, do not add an *-er* or *-est* ending.

> **Examples:** **powerful   more powerful (the) most powerful**

Grammar, Mechanics, and Usage
Comparing with Adjectives and Adverbs (continued)

Usually, adverbs end in the letters -*ly*. Before adverbs ending in -*ly*, use *more* to compare two actions. Use *most* to compare more than two.

Examples:

quickly   more quickly   (the) most quickly

No Comparison:	Lee works <u>quickly</u>.
Comparing Two:	Tim works <u>more quickly</u> than Lee.
Comparing More Than Two:	Alan works the <u>most quickly</u> of all.

A few adverbs do not end in -*ly*. To these adverbs, add the ending -*er* to compare two actions. Add the ending -*est* to compare more than two.

Examples:

hard   harder   (the) hardest

The spelling of an adjective or an adverb may change when you add the ending -*er* or -*est*.

Examples: big   bigger   (the) biggest

Writer's Handbook

Grammar, Mechanics, and Usage

Showing Where, When, and How (Prepositions)

Rule: Some words are used to show where something is. Other words help show when or how something happened. These words are called **prepositions.** Prepositions are not used alone.

Prepositions are used with nouns. The nouns usually come after the preposition.

> **Prepositions:**
>
> in the house   around the corner
> after lunch   from Pat

A preposition can show **where** something is or where something happens.

> **Where:** The bag is on the table.
>   Jacob reached into the bag.

A preposition can show **when** something happens or happened.

> **When:** I saw Brianna after school.

Grammar, Mechanics, and Usage

Showing Where, When, and How (continued)

Some prepositions tell **how** something happens or happened.

How: Larry cut the paper <u>with</u> scissors.

Here are some prepositions you can use in your writing. Use prepositions with nouns.

above	before	during	to
after	behind	in	until
around	by	near	with

Writer's Handbook

Grammar, Mechanics, and Usage

Showing That Story Characters Are Talking (Dialogue)

Rule: In a story, what characters say to each other is called **dialogue.** A speaker's exact words are called a quotation. These words are put inside quotation marks (" ").

Place quotation marks (" ") before and after a speaker's exact words.

Quotation Marks:
"It's a beautiful day," said Brian.

Begin the first word of a quotation with a capital letter, even if it is not at the beginning of a sentence.

Capital Letters:
"Let's go back to the beach," said Kim.
Brian said, "We can't go to the beach today."

Use a comma to separate a quotation from the rest of the sentence.

Commas:
"The beach would be fun," said Kim.
Brian replied, "But today is a school day."

Grammar, Mechanics, and Usage
Showing That Story Characters Are Talking (Dialogue) (continued)

Words such as *said Kim* tell who is speaking. They are called speaker tags.

Put the end mark for the quotation inside the closing quotation marks.

End Marks:
Kim snapped, "Let's check a calendar."
"Go ahead and check," said Brian.
"Yes, it's a beach day!" Kim exclaimed.
"Are you joking?" asked Brian.

Writer's Handbook

Study Skills

Parts of a Book

All books have a **title page** and a **copyright page.** Some books also have a **table of contents, glossary,** and **index.**

You don't always have to read a whole book to find information. Use the parts of a book to find only the information you need. The parts of a book can help you find out what the book is about, the page on which stories or articles begin, and the meaning of new words.

The **title page** is usually the first printed page at the front of the book. It gives

- the title
- the name of the author or editor
- the name of the publisher

The **copyright** comes after the title page. It gives

- the publisher's name
- the place and year the book was published

The **table of contents** is a list of each unit, story, or chapter in the book and the number of the page on which each begins.

Study Skills
Parts of a Book (continued)

The **glossary** is a list of new or special words used in the book. It has

- words, their definitions, and sometimes their pronunciations, listed in ABC order

The **index** is a list of names, places, and topics found in the book. It has

- names, places, and topics, listed in ABC order
- page numbers for each mention of the name, place, or topic

Writer's Handbook

Study Skills

Alphabetical Order

Alphabetical order, or **ABC order,** means that the words are put in the same order as the letters of the alphabet. When you put words in ABC order, think about the order of the letters of the alphabet.

The words in dictionaries, encyclopedias, card catalogs, indexes, and glossaries are listed in ABC order. Knowing the rules for ABC order will help you find and list information more easily.

- When words start with different letters, use the first letter of each word to put the words in ABC order.

  Start with Different Letters:
  cat   horse   lion

- When words have the same first letter, use the next letter that is different in each word to put the words in ABC order.

  Start with Same Letter:
  deer   dog   duck

- If *a*, *an*, or *the* is the first word of a title, do not use it. Instead, use the first letter of the second word.

Study Skills
Alphabetical Order (continued)

Start with *A*, *An*, or *The*:
The Empty Pot
A Pair of Red Clogs
The Tale of Peter Rabbit

■ When you look up or list names, use the first letter of the person's last name. Often people's names are listed with the last name first.

Last Name First: Lobel, Arnold
Matsumo, Masako
Yashima, Taro

Writer's Handbook

Study Skills

Using a Dictionary or Glossary

A **dictionary** is a book that gives meanings for the words you use every day when you speak, write, or read. A **glossary** is the part of a book that gives the meaning of words you find in that book.

- The words in a dictionary or glossary are listed in ABC order. They are also printed in dark type. These words are called **entry words.** If you were looking for the entry word *feast*, you would look for the letter *f*.

- At the top of each page of a dictionary are two words called **guide words.** Guide words show the first and last entry words on that page. Only entry words that come between those two words in ABC order will be found on that page. For example, *feast* would come between the guide words *entry* and *generous*.

Study Skills
Using a Dictionary or Glossary (continued)

Use dictionaries and glossaries to find the meanings of new words you read. Check words in a dictionary when you proofread your own writing. This is what an entry for *feast* might look in a dictionary or glossary.

> **feast** (fēst) *v.* to eat very well; to eat a lot of good food. —*n.* A large, fancy meal.

- The information in the entry tells how the word is pronounced (fēst), what part of speech it is (*v.* and *n.*), and what meanings the word has.

A dictionary entry for a word tells much more about the word than a glossary entry does. A glossary entry tells only the meaning of the word as it is used in that book.

Writer's Handbook

Study Skills

Using an Encyclopedia

An **encyclopedia** is one or more books that contain information on many subjects. Each book in a set is called a volume. The subjects within are usually arranged in ABC order. Each volume is marked to show what subjects are inside. Some encyclopedias use numbers as marks; others use letters. In a set, one volume is usually an index.

An encyclopedia is a good place to find information about a subject. To use it, follow these guidelines.

- Think about your subject. What is the most important word in your subject? For example, if you want to find out how the pilgrims lived, *pilgrims* is the most important word. If your subject is a person, look for information under the person's last name.

  Examples: Pilgrims   Washington, George

Study Skills

Using an Encyclopedia (continued)

■ If your encyclopedia has an index, look up the word there. Next to the word you look up, you will see a volume number or letter, a colon (:), and a page number.

Examples: Washington, George 23:95
(or W:19)

This tells you that there is an article about George Washington in volume 23, beginning on page 95 (or in volume W, beginning on page 19).

■ Find the volume you need, then turn to the page. Read through the article and take notes on the most important information about your subject.

■ At the end of the article, you may see a list of other articles in the encyclopedia. These articles may have more information about your subject.

Example: *See also* **Mount Vernon; Revolutionary War.**

Writer's Handbook

Study Skills

Using Maps

Maps are drawings that show where places and things, such as rivers, mountains, cities, roads, parks, and buildings, can be found. A book of maps is called an **atlas.** A **globe** shows the round shape of the world and has on it a map of the Earth.

On a map, lines, colors, and pictures are used to show things. Here are some guidelines for using maps.

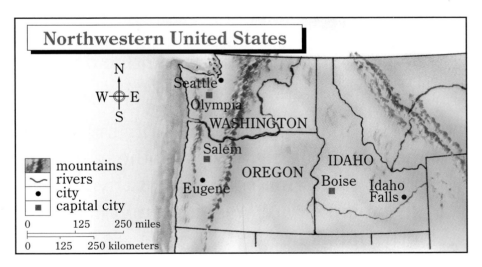

- Read the **title.** The title of a map tells what the map shows. This map is a map of the northwestern United States.

Study Skills
Using Maps (continued)

- Find the **map key.** The map key shows the special pictures, lines, and colors that are used on the map. Here are the pictures that are used for the map on page 409.

    mountains   ● city

    river   ■ capital city

- Look at the **direction arrows.** These show north, south, east, and west on the map. North is usually toward the top of the map. This means that south is toward the bottom, east is to the right, and west is to the left.

- Use the map key and direction arrows to find out about the places on the map. For example, this map shows that Olympia is the capital city of Washington. It is located north of Salem.

Writer's Handbook

Study Skills

Looking Up Information

There are many ways to find information. You can find it by reading, talking to people, or visiting museums. You will spend less time looking for facts if you know where to look.

When you are doing research, decide where the best place is to find the kinds of facts you need. Here are some places to find information.

- An **atlas** is a book of maps. Use an atlas if you need to find out about a continent, country, state, or city. You can also find out about oceans, rivers, or mountains.

- A **dictionary** is a book that lists words in ABC order. Use a dictionary if you need to find the spellings and meanings of words and how to say them.

- An **encyclopedia** is a set of books that contains facts on many subjects. The subjects are in ABC order. You can find many useful facts in an encyclopedia article.

- **Magazines** and **newspapers** contain many facts. You can get the most up-to-date information from them.

- A **nonfiction book** presents facts on a topic. You may read the whole book for information, or you may take facts from a few pages of the book.

- An **interview** means talking with someone and asking questions to find out facts.

- A **museum** can give facts on a special subject. A museum has exhibits and books. At a museum, you can also talk to people who know about a subject.

Writer's Handbook

Study Skills

Finding Books in a Library

Each library has a **catalog**—a list of all the books in a library. The catalog lists each book three ways: by the author's name, by the title of the book, and by the subject of the book.

The catalog helps you quickly find books in your library. It is a good place to start your research. To find books in a library, you should know the following information:

- The catalog may be on cards or on a computer. If it is on cards, small file drawers hold the cards in ABC order. If it is on a computer, the catalog will contain the same kind of information that the cards contain.

- The catalog has three types of cards or ways to look for a book. An **author** card is filed by the author's name, last name first. A **title** card is filed by the book's title. A **subject** card is filed by the subject of the book. You can look up an author's name, a book title, or a subject.

- The entry for a book contains a **call number.** This number helps you find which shelf the book belongs on.

- The entry names the **publisher,** the company that made the book. It also shows where and when the book was made.

- The entry tells how many pages the book has and whether it has pictures.

- An entry often tells what the book is about. You can use the summary to help you decide whether the book has the information you need.

Writer's Handbook

Study Skills

Understanding and Making a Time Line

A **time line** shows the order in which important events happened over a specific period of time. It can help readers understand important facts. A time line may be as long or as short as it needs to be. It may cover one year, a hundred years, or thousands of years.

Making a time line can help you present important facts from your research. Here are guidelines for making a time line.

■ Decide what you want to show in your time line. Choose a title for it.

  Example: How My Plant Grew

■ Make a list of the main events and the time of each one. Use short phrases.

  Examples: Planted seed—March
  Sprout came up—April
  Leaves came out—May
  Plant bloomed—June

■ Draw a line across a sheet of paper. Above and below the line, leave space for writing the events and the times—in order, going from left to right.

Study Skills

Understanding and Making a Time Line (continued)

- On the line, make a dot for the time of each event. Make the space between the dots different, according to the length of time between events.

- Below each dot, write a time.

- Above each dot, write an event.

Planted seed	Sprout came up	Leaves came out	Plant bloomed
●	●	●	●
March	April	May	June

Writer's Handbook

Study Skills

Understanding and Making a Chart

A **chart** can show a lot of information in a little space. Words or numbers are written in boxes to help readers find information quickly.

Many books and magazines use charts. You can use them in your own writing. Then you can show a lot of information clearly. The following information will help you understand and make charts.

- A chart shows the same kind of information about several different things. For example, a chart might show information about some different vegetables: their colors, their shapes, and which part of the plant they are.

Vegetables			
Name	*Color*	*Shape*	*Part*
peas	green	round	seeds
carrots	orange	long, thin	roots
beets	reddish	round	roots

Study Skills

- A chart has a title that tells what it is about.

- Headings across the top of the chart tell what kinds of information will be shown about each thing.

- Headings that are written down the left side of the chart show what things will be described.

- Lines make the chart easy to read. The lines make boxes.

- Words or numbers—not sentences—are inside the boxes.

Writer's Handbook

Writing and Technology

Using a Word Processor

A **word processor** is a special kind of computer program. It is a program that helps you create, edit, save, and print written works.

There are many types of word processors. Each looks a little different from the others. However, almost all word processing programs allow you to do certain tasks. These tasks include the following:

- You can start a **new** piece of writing. You will then see a blank white part of the screen. In most programs, do this by selecting the command NEW on the FILE menu.

- You can work on an existing piece of writing. To do this, you **open** a file that was made at an earlier time. In most programs, do this by selecting the command OPEN on the FILE menu.

- You can type text. Just click on the white screen and start to **type.**

- You can change or **edit** text. To add words, click on the place where you want the words. Then type them. To take out words, first select them with the mouse. Then tap the delete or backspace (⇐) key.

Writing and Technology
Using a Word Processor (continued)

- You can **save** your work on a disk or on the computer. In most programs, do this by selecting the command SAVE on the FILE menu.

- You can **print** your work. In most programs, do this by selecting the command PRINT on the FILE menu.

Writer's Handbook

Writing and Technology

Using an On-Line Encyclopedia

An **on-line encyclopedia** contains information on many subjects. The subjects within it are usually arranged in ABC order. An on-line encyclopedia is a good place to find information about a number of subjects.

Most encyclopedias use **search tools.** These are programs that find information. There are different kinds of search tools, but these guidelines will help you use most of them:

- Think about your subject. What is the most important word in your subject? For example, if you want to find out when Texas became a state, *Texas* is the most important word. If your subject is a person, look for information under the person's last name.
  Examples: Texas   O'Keeffe, Georgia

- Type a word or short phrase into the empty box on the search tool screen. Make sure that your spelling is correct. Then click SEARCH or FIND.

- You will usually see a list of articles that contain the word or phrase you typed. Click on any title that you want to read.

- If you do not get a list of articles, try using a different word. For example, if the word *painter* does not work, try *artist*.

- If you get a list of articles that is very long, try adding another word to the box on the search tool. For example, instead of *government*, try *state government*.

- Often, an article will contain links to related articles. A link looks like an underlined word or phrase. Often it is a different color from the other text. When you click on a link, a new article or screen will appear.

- Use the BACK button or arrow (⇐) to return to a screen that you saw earlier.

Many on-line encyclopedias allow you to print articles. This is useful because it allows you to read articles later, when you are not using the computer.

Writer's Handbook

Writing and Technology

On-Line Safety Tips

Computers can connect you to the whole world. Many people use computers to communicate with others on-line. They communicate by E-mail and by meeting in areas called chat rooms.

You can have fun meeting people on-line. You can also learn about different places. However, when you meet people on-line, you need to follow certain safety rules.

- Never believe everything you read on-line. Remember that many people make up things about themselves on-line. For example, they might pretend to be older or younger than they really are. They may pretend to have another name.

- Never give out personal information on-line. Do not give your whole name or your address. Do not give your phone number or the name of your school. If someone asks for this information, tell an adult.

- Never give out your password. Do not even tell it to your friends.

Writing and Technology

On-Line Safety Tips (continued)

- Never agree to meet anyone in person unless you first tell an adult. Make sure to get the adult's permission.

- Never send a picture of yourself to someone you don't know. If someone asks for a picture, check with an adult.

Safety rules are important. In person, you know that you should be careful about strangers. On-line, you should follow the same rules.

Glossary

A

advice (əd vīs´) *n.* Someone's opinion of what another should do.

allergic (ə lûr´ jik) *adj.* Having an annoying or dangerous reaction to something.

Anasazi (o´ nə so´ zē) *n.* Prehistoric Native Americans who lived in the canyon areas of what is now Arizona and New Mexico.

antelope (an´ təl ōp´) *n.* An animal similar to a deer.

anvil (an´ vəl) *n.* A heavy metal block on which hot metal is hammered and shaped.

avalanche (av´ ə lanch´) *n.* A large amount of snow, ice, or stones falling rapidly down the side of a mountain.

axle (ak´ səl) *n.* A rod on which the wheels of a wagon turn.

Pronunciation **a**t; l**ā**te; c**â**re; f**ä**ther; s**e**t; m**ē**; **i**t; k**ī**te; **o**x; r**ō**se; **ô** in b**ou**ght; **coi**n; b**oo**k; t**oo**; f**o**rm; **ou**t; **u**p; **ū**se; t**u**rn; **ə** sound in **a**bout, chick**e**n, penc**i**l, cann**o**n, circ**u**s; **ch**air; **hw** in **wh**ich; ri**ng**; **sh**op; **th**in; t**h**ere; **zh** in treasure.

B

bead (bēd) *v.* To make something by stringing beads together.

beam (bēm) *n.* A ray of light.

big house (big hous) *n.* The house on a plantation in which the owner of the plantation lives.

blacksmith (blak´ smith´) *n.* A person who makes things out of iron.

borne (born) *v.* Past tense of **bear:** to hold up; to carry.

burrow (bûr´ ō) *v.* To dig a tunnel in the earth.

bustling (bus´ ling) *adj.* Filled with activity.

by and by (bī ənd bī) *adv.* Soon.

C

canyon (kan´ yən) *n.* A deep, narrow valley.

chamber (chām´ bər) *n.* A room.

character (kar´ ik tər) *n.* A person's honesty and honor.

charm (chärm) *n.* An object worn to bring good luck.

chorus (kor´ əs) *v.* To say all together as one voice.

climate (klī´ mit) *n.* The weather in an area.

coil (koil) *v.* To wind a long, thin rope of something around and around in a circle.

colony (ko´ lə nē) *n.* A group of people living in a new area who still have a connection to their home country.

colossal (kə los´ əl) *adj.* Huge; very, very big.

counterpane (koun´ tər pān´) *n.* A bed covering.

courtyard (kort´ yärd) *n.* An open space surrounded by walls or buildings.

cradle board (krā´ dəl bord) *n.* A board on which an infant is tied and carried on someone's back.

crinkle (kring´ kəl) *v.* To scrunch up; wrinkle.

D

dangle (dang´ gəl) *v.* To hang loosely.

declare (di klâr´) *v.* To say in an official way.

demand (di mand´) *v.* To say that something should belong to one; to claim as one's own.

depend (di pend´) *v.* To trust; to count on someone for help.

dike (dīk) *n.* A thick wall built to hold back water.

dinosaur (dīn´ ə sôr) *n.* Any of the large group of extinct, prehistoric animals that lived long ago.

disappear (dis´ ə pēr´) *v.* 1. To leave someone's sight; to stop being seen. 2. To stop living.

DJ *n.* A radio disc jockey.

doctorate (dok´ tər it) *n.* An award for graduating from the highest level of college; a doctoral degree.

doe (dō) *n.* A female deer.

dozen (du´ zən) *n.* Twelve.

dread (dred) *v.* To feel fearful or unhappy about something.

drench (drench) *v.* To soak with water.

drinking gourd (dring´ king gord) *n.* The hard-shelled fruit of a vining plant that is hollowed out and used to dip water.

drinking gourd

dwelling (dwel´ ling) *n.* A place where one lives.

E

earthquake (ûrth′ kwāk′) *n.*
An underground shock that
makes part of the Earth's
surface shake.

echo (ek′ ō) *n.* A sound that
seems to be repeated because it
is thrown back from far away.

elk (elk) *n.* A large member of
the deer family.

embed (em bed′) *v.* To set
something into a material.

emblem (em′ bləm) *n.* Sign;
symbol.

enormous (i nôr′ məs) *adj.*
Huge; very big.

enrich (in rich′) *v.* To make
better.

erupt (i rupt′) *v.* To burst out;
to explode.

exclaim (ik sklām′) *v.* To cry
out suddenly.

explorer (ik splor′ ər) *n.*
Someone who travels through
new lands to learn about them.

extinct (ek stingkt′) *adj.* No
longer existing.

F

ferry (fâr′ ē) *n.* A medium-size
boat or raft. —*v.* To carry
something over water by boat.

flood (flud) *v.* To cover with
water.

folk art (fōk′ ärt) *n.* Art that
shows the interests, traditions,
or lifestyles of the people who
create it.

ford (ford) *v.* To cross directly
through the water of a river.

forge (forj) *n.* A workshop that
makes objects out of metal
heated in a large furnace.

fortunately (for′ chə nət lē)
adv. With luck; luckily.

fossil (fos′ əl) *n.* The hardened
remains or traces of an animal
or plant that lived long ago.

fret (fret) *v.* To worry.

G

gleaming (glēm´ ing) *adj.* Shining brightly.

gurgling (gûr´ gling) *adj.* Making a noise like bubbling water.

guts (guts) *n. slang.* Courage; bravery.

H

handsome (han´ səm) *adj.* Pleasing to look at; good-looking.

hearth (härth) *n.* Fireplace.

hero (hēr´ ō) *n.* A person who does brave or important things to help others.

homesick (hōm´ sik´) *adj.* Sad due to wanting to go home; missing one's home.

huddled (hu´ dəld) *adj.* Gathered together closely.

I

Iguanodon (i gwä´ nə don´) *n.* A dinosaur that walked on two feet and ate only plants.

imprint (im print´) *v.* To make a mark by pressing.

indentured servant (in den´ chərd sûr´ vənt) *n.* A person who agrees in a contract to work for a certain length of time in exchange for some sort of payment.

independence (in´ də pen´ dəns) *n.* Not being under the control of others; freedom.

international (in´ tər nash´ ə nəl) *adj.* Having to do with two or more nations.

issue (ish´ o͞o) *v.* To publish; to send out.

J

jalapeño (ho´ lə pā´ nyō) *n.* A Mexican hot pepper.

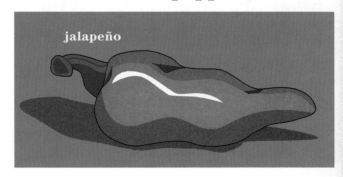

jalapeño

juniper (jo͞o´ nə pər) *n.* A cone-bearing tree or shrub in the cypress family.

> **Pronunciation at; lāte; câre; fäther; set; mē; it; kīte; ox; rōse; ô in bought; coin; bŏŏk; tōō; form; out; up; ūse; turn; ə sound in about, chicken, pencil, cannon, circus; chair; hw in which; ring; shop; thin; thēere; zh in treasure.**

K

kiva (kē′ və) *n.* A round structure used by the Pueblo for special ceremonies.

knead (nēd) *v.* To form into a ball and press over and over with the hands.

L

lack (lak) *n.* A need; a shortage; not enough of something.

livestock (līv′ stok) *n.* Farm animals, such as cows, sheep, horses, or pigs. —*adj.* Having to do with such animals.

lob (lob) *v.* To throw easily and slowly.

M

mammoth (mam′ əth) *n.* A large, hairy elephant that lived long ago.

mass (mas) *n.* A large group of people.

merchant (mûr′ chənt) *n.* Someone who sells things.

mesa (mā′ sə) *n.* A large, flat raised-up area of land.

minister (min′ ə stər) *n.* 1. A person who helps a king or queen rule. 2. A pastor; the leader in a church.

moccasin (mo′ kə sən) *n.* A soft shoe made of deerskin, first made and worn by Native Americans.

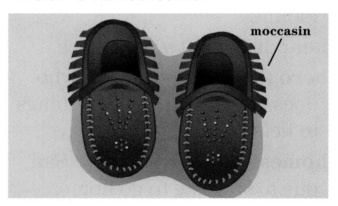

moccasin

monument (mon′ yə mənt) *n.* A structure built to honor someone or something important.

mural (myûr′ əl) *n.* A large painting, often on a wall.

mutter (mu′ tər) *v.* To say something angrily loud enough for only the speaker to hear.

mysterious (mis tēr′ ē əs) *adj.* Making others curious or surprised; causing others to wonder.

N

numb (num) *adj.* Having no feeling; not able to feel anything in some part of the body.

O

oath (ōth) *n.* A promise to tell the truth.

oblige (ə blīj′) *v.* To agree to do something for someone.

ooze (ōōz) *n.* Slush; slime; watery mud.

overstuffed (ō′ vər stuft′) *adj.* Having more in it than it can easily hold.

P

paleontologist (pā′ lē ən tol′ ə jist) *n.* A scientist who studies the fossils of prehistoric animal and plant life.

pedestal (pe′ dəs təl) *n.* A base that something sits on.

peg (peg) *n.* A piece of wood used to hang things on.

petitioner (pə ti′ shən ər) *n.* Someone who asks some level of government for something.

pinky (ping′ kē) *n.* The little finger on a person's hand; the finger farthest from the thumb.

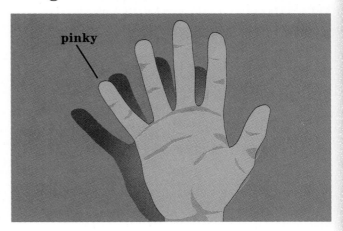

pinyon (pin′ yōn′) *n.* A low-growing pine that bears seeds that can be eaten.

plait (plāt) *v.* To twist and weave strands of a material into one piece; to braid.

plantation (plan tā′ shən) *n.* A very large farm where crops like rice, cotton, or sugar are grown.

platter (pla′ tər) *n.* A large plate.

prehistoric (prē´ hi stor´ ik) *adj.* Belonging to a time many years ago, before history was written down.

prejudice (prej´ ə dis) *n.* Unfairness; an opinion formed without knowing the facts.

proclamation (prok´ lə mā´ shən) *n.* A public announcement; a statement to the people.

prodigious (prə dij´ əs) *adj.* Enormous; monstrous.

protest (prō´ test) *n.* A public demonstration of objection.

Pueblo (pwe´ blō) *n.* A Native American group from the southwestern part of the United States.

Q

qualify (kwô´ lə fī´) *v.* To have the knowledge needed to do a certain task.

R

refuse (ri fyo͞oz´) *v.* To have an unwillingness to accept.

religion (ri li´ jən) *n.* A set of beliefs and practices based on teachings of a spiritual leader.

remembrance (ri mem´ brəns) *n.* An object meant to remind one of something good.

reply (ri plī´) *v.* To answer.

reservation (re´ zər vā´ shən) *n.* A piece of public land set aside for Native Americans.

resound (ri zound´) *v.* To say loudly.

reverse (ri vûrs´) *n.* The opposite way; backward.

revolution (re´ və lo͞o´ shən) *n.* Overthrowing a government often through violence; war.

rumble (rum´ bəl) *v.* To make a low, rolling sound like thunder.

S

scientist (sī´ ən tist) *n.* A person who studies nature and natural laws.

scroll (skrōl) *n.* A roll of paper used for writing, especially many years ago.

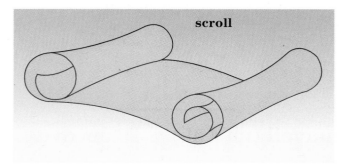

scroll

Seismosaurus (sīs´ mə sor´ əs) *n.* A dinosaur that was about 110 feet long and 50 feet tall.

shallow (shal´ ō) *adj.* Not deep.

shoo (sho͞o) *v.* To go away.

Shoshone (shə shō´ nē) *n.* A Native American group originally from the western United States. —*adj.* Having to do with this group.

shove (shuv) *v.* To push with force.

shuffle (shu´ fəl) *v.* To mix together in a confused way.

slat (slat) *n.* A flat strip of wood.

slot (slot) *n.* A long, thin opening.

soot (so͝ot) *n.* Tiny, black bits of something that has burned, such as wood or coal.

sought (sôt) *v.* A past tense of **seek**: To look for; to try to find.

spirit (spēr´ ət) *n.* An unseen being or force that guides and watches out for another.

sprinkler (spring´ klər) *n.* A device that scatters drops of water.

stable (stā´ bəl) *n.* A building in which tame animals, especially horses, are kept.

stoop (sto͞op) *v.* To bend over.

stupendous (stə pen´ dəs) *adj.* Amazingly large.

sturdy (stûr´ dē) *adj.* Well built; very strong; not easily broken.

succeed (sək sēd´) *v.* To take someone's job after that person quits; to follow in a job after someone else.

successor (sək ses´ ər) *n.* A person who takes over another person's job.

swamp (swomp) *n.* An area of low, wet ground; a marsh.

swampy (swom´ pē) *adj.* Having wetness most of the time.

> **Pronunciation** at; lāte; câre; fäther; set; mē; it; kīte; ox; rōse; ô in bought; coin; bŏŏk; tōō; form; out; up; ūse; turn; ə sound in about, chicken, pencil, cannon, circus; chair; hw in which; ring; shop; thin; ŧħere; zh in treasure.

swat (swot) *v.* To hit with a quick, hard blow.

swirl (swûrl) *v.* To spin around; to turn around rapidly.

T

tannery (ta′ nə rē) *n.* A place where animal skins are treated to become leather.

tempest-tossed (tem′ pəst tost) *adj.* Thrown around by a storm; storm-tossed.

tend (tend) *v.* To take care of; to care for.

titanic (tī tan′ ik) *adj.* Great in size or power.

tourist (tōŏr′ ist) *n.* Someone who visits a place.

transfer (trans fûr′) *v.* To move something from one place to another.

tremble (trem′ bəl) *v.* To shake; to shiver.

tremendous (tri men′ dəs) *adj.* Enormous; huge.

trickle (trik′ əl) *v.* To flow in a small stream.

U

unveil (un′ vāl′) *v.* To uncover.

V

vendor (ven′ dər) *n.* Someone who sells things; seller.

volcano (vol kā′ nō) *n.* A hole in the earth that throws out smoke, melted rock, and ashes, forming a mountain.

volcano

W

water bug (wô′ tər bug′) *n.* A very large, slow-moving insect.

weary (wēr′ ē) *adj.* Very tired.

wimp (wimp) *n. slang.* A person who is weak and afraid.

windmill (wind´ mil) *n.* A tall structure with sails on poles, or "arms," that stick out from the top and spin around using the power of the wind. When the arms spin, a machine inside grinds up grain or pumps water.

windmill

wither (wi´ t**h**ər) *v.* To dry up.

wordless (wûrd´ lis) *adj.* Silent.

Y

yearn (yûrn) *v.* To wish for.

Yiddish (yi´ dəsh) *n.* A Jewish language.

yon (yon) *adv.* Yonder; over there.

yucca (yu´ kə) *n.* A desert plant that has spiky leaves and gets a tall stalk with whitish flowers on it.

Acknowledgments *continued*

Photo Credits

14 15 Tom Bean/Corbis; **16** Jonathan Blair/Corbis; **17** David Mueuch/Corbis; **18-19** James L. Amos/Corbis; **20** Jim Sugar Photography/Corbis; **22-23** Gail Mooney/Corbis; **21** Richard T. Nowitz/Corbis; **24** David Muench/Corbis; **25** Annie Griffiths Belt/Corbis; **26 27** Layne Kennedy/Corbis; **30** Michael S. Yamashita/Corbis; **31** Dorling Kindersley Limited, London/Corbis; **32** © Dave Chare Photography; **132 b** © Sigrid Estrada; **151** Robin Nelson/Black Star; **168** © Peter Ziebel; **208** Courtesy of the Library of Congress; **209** Corbis-Bettmann; **210** The Granger Collection, New York; **211** The Granger Collection, New York; **212** Corbis-Bettmann; **213** Courtesy of the Library of Congress; **214** Corbis-Bettmann; **215** The Granger Collection, New York; **216 217** Courtesy of the Library of Congress; **218** The Granger Collection, New York; **219 220** Courtesy of the Library of Congress; **221** North Wind Pictures; **222** The Granger Collection, New York; **223** North Wind Pictures; **224** Courtesy of the Library of Congress; **225** The Granger Collection, New York; **226b** Courtesy of the Library of Congress; **226t** PhotoDisc; **227** North Wind Pictures; **228** Courtesy of the Library of Congress; **229 230** UPI/Corbis-Bettmann; **231** David Frazier/Tony Stone Images, Inc.; **232** Lowell Georgia/Photo Researchers, Inc; **233** Carol Kitman; **234** UPI/Corbis-Bettmann; **235 l** M.K. Denny/PhotoEdit, **r** Tom McCarthey/PhotoEdit, **b** Ed Young/Science Photo Library/Photo Researchers, Inc.; **279** Jean Miele/The Stock Market; **352** © Rosmarie Hausherr.

Art Acknowledgments

Unit 4 (Fossils) Ed Miller
Unit 5 (Courage) Sylvie Wickstrom
Unit 6 (Our Country and Its People) Elizabeth Wolf